Bridging the Gap

Between
Common Core State Standards
and Teaching Statistics

Pat Hopfensperger
University of Wisconsin-Milwaukee

Tim Jacobbe
University of Florida

Deborah Lurie
Saint Joseph's University

Jerry Moreno
John Carroll University

Second Printing

NATIONAL COUNCIL OF
TEACHERS OF MATHEMATICS

Production Team

Pat Hopfensperger
Associate Editor

Jerry Moreno
Editor

Rebecca Nichols
R Programmer

Valerie Nirala
*Designer and Editorial Production
Manager*

©2012 by American Statistical Association
Alexandria, VA 22314-1943

Printed in the United States of America
10 9 8 7 6 5 4 3 2 1

978-0-9839375-1-7

Library of Congress Cataloging-in-Publication Data

Bridging the gap between common core state standards and teaching statistics
/ Pat Hopfensperger ... [et al.].
   p. cm.
 ISBN 978-0-9839375-1-7
 1. Mathematical statistics--Study and teaching (Elementary)--Standards-
-United Sttes. 2. Mathematical statistics--Study and teaching (Middle
school)--Standards--United Sttes. I. Hopfensperger, Patrick.
 QA276.13.B75 2012
 519.5071'273--dc23
               2012011291

In memory of

Martha Aliaga

whose passion and love for statistics education
have been and will continue to be
an inspiration for us all to follow.

TABLE OF CONTENTS

FOREWORD

I am honored to write the foreword for *Bridging the Gap Between Common Core State Standards and Teaching Statistics* (*BTG*), a collection of data-centric activities for elementary and middle-school students. As statistics is being recognized as a necessary component in the K–12 mathematics curriculum, there is an urgency for the development of materials such as *BTG*. This urgency is most immediate with the Common Core State Standards (CCSS), in which statistics is one of the major components (alongside algebra and geometry).

How did statistics come to be a part of the K–12 mathematics curriculum? In its *Principles and Standards for School Mathematics* (*PSSM*), the National Council of Teachers of Mathematics (NCTM) articulated a vision for mathematics education that included data analysis and probability as one of five major content strands. NCTM's Data Analysis and Probability standard states the following:

> Instructional programs from pre-kindergarten through Grade 12 should enable all students to—
>
> - Formulate questions that can be addressed with data and collect, organize, and display relevant data to answer them
>
> - Select and use appropriate statistical methods to analyze data
>
> - Develop and evaluate inferences and predictions based on data
>
> - Understand and apply basic concepts of probability

To support and further elaborate on the Data Analysis and Probability standard, the ASA/NCTM Joint Committee on Curriculum in Statistics and Probability (JC) produced *Guidelines for Assessment and Instruction in Statistics Education (GAISE): A Pre-K–12 Curriculum Framework*, which was endorsed by the American Statistical Association (ASA) in 2005 (*www.amstat.org/education/gaise*). The JC, in 2007, worked with the authors of the GAISE framework to incorporate final editing and provide funding for printing the report in book format.

What motivated the development of the GAISE Pre-K–12 framework? In NCTM's PSSM, the concept of the mean is discussed at the elementary, middle, and secondary levels. In 2003, the ASA sponsored the TEAM's conference, held at the University of Georgia. Johnny Lott, a keynote speaker and then president of NCTM, asked the statisticians, "What is going on in statistics if you are doing the mean at all three levels? Are you doing the same thing?" These questions led a group of writers to author the GAISE report over a two-year period.

Goals of the GAISE framework are to:

- Present the statistics curriculum for grades pre-K–12 as a cohesive and coherent curriculum strand (e.g., the progression of the mean from elementary to middle to secondary)

- Promote and develop statistical literacy

- Provide links with the NCTM standards

- Discuss differences between mathematical and statistical thinking, particularly the importance of context and variability within statistical thinking

- Clarify the role of probability in statistics

- Illustrate concepts associated with the data analysis process

Why data analysis in K–12? The GAISE framework answers this question as the following:

> Every high-school graduate should be able to use sound statistical reasoning to intelligently cope with the requirements of citizenship, employment, and family and to be prepared for a healthy and productive life. Statistics education can promote the 'must-have' competencies for high-school graduates to 'thrive in this modern world of mass information.'

Let's not forget the intellectual merit of statistics thinking. The well-known mathematician George Polya said, "Plausible reasoning—the inferential reasoning of science and everyday life by which new knowledge is obtained— is an important part of mathematical reasoning."

The GAISE framework outlines the conceptual structure for statistics education in a two-dimensional model with one dimension defined by the four-step problem solving process (formulate questions, collect data, analyze data, and interpret results) plus the nature of variability. The second dimension is comprised of three levels of statistical development (levels A, B, and C) that students must progress through to develop statistical understanding. Grade ranges for attainment of each level are intentionally unspecified. Students must begin and master the concepts at Level A before moving on to levels B and C. It is paramount for students to have worthwhile experiences at levels

A and B during their elementary school years to prepare for future development at Level C at the secondary level. Without such experiences, a middle- [or high-] school student who has had no prior experience with statistics will need to begin with Level A concepts and activities before moving to Level B.

The GAISE framework has become instrumental in providing guidance to writers of national mathematics documents, writers of state standards, writers of assessment items, curriculum directors, pre-K–12 teachers, and faculty of teacher preparation colleges on the essential topics and concepts in data analysis and probability for all students as they progress from kindergarten to graduation from high school. The GAISE framework has influenced the statistics components of both the Mathematics and Statistics College Board Standards for College Success (2007) and the NCTM document *Focus in High School Mathematics* (2008). The GAISE framework also influenced the data analysis and probability strand of recent state mathematics standard revisions (which includes my home state of Georgia). Most recently, the GAISE framework was the basis for the statistics and probability component included in the Common Core State Standards in mathematics.

Bridging the Gap is an excellent classroom resource that follows both the GAISE framework and Common Core State Standards for grades K–8. The elementary and middle grades are critical in laying the foundation of skills needed for our students to grow and evolve into sound statistical thinkers. These activities bring the real world to the student and provide the student the opportunity to understand the necessity of statistical reasoning and sense making for everyday life and post-secondary education. I'm appreciative to the writers of *BTG* and the ASA/NCTM Joint Committee for developing this valuable resource in support of both the recommendations of GAISE, the recommendations of the Common Core State Standards, and the importance of statistical reasoning in our K–8 curriculum.

Christine Franklin, University of Georgia
Chair of the GAISE report for grades pre-K–12

ACKNOWLEDGMENTS

We are indebted to the ASA/NCTM Joint Committee on Curriculum in Statistics and Probability (JC) for its support throughout the process of creating and publishing *Bridging the Gap* (*BTG*). This project began at a workshop held in the summer of 2008 at The Lawrenceville School in New Jersey. Its initial purpose was to begin the writing of classroom activities at levels A, B, and C of the GAISE framework. Several writings from the workshop formed the basis for the *BTG* investigations. Heartfelt thanks are extended to the workshop participants: Gloria Barrett, Cindy Bryant, Tim Erickson, Bonnie Hagelberger, Katherine Halvorsen, Pat Hopfensperger, Tim Jacobbe, Sibel Kazak, Michael Kimmel, Henry Kranendonk, Jim Landwehr, Mike Perry, Dick Scheaffer, and Daren Starnes.

As the Common Core State Standards (CCSS) in mathematics were initiated and the JC published *Making Sense of Statistical Studies* (15 high-school activities on surveys, observational studies, and experiments), it was decided that *BTG* should focus on only GAISE levels A and B and connect them to the CCSS for elementary and middle childhood.

In 2009, the JC approved Tim Jacobbe, Deborah Lurie, Pat Hopfensperger, and Jerry Moreno as the main writers of *BTG*. Some of the investigations are based on those initiated by the "Lawrenceville Group"; others are based on activities in the Data-Driven Mathematics series and *Exploring Statistics in the Elementary Grades*. We are also thankful for Tena Katsaounis, who contributed "What Do Frogs Eat?"

Sincere thanks are extended to Christine Franklin for her support expressed in the foreword, Katherine Halvorsen for her section on clarifying what constitutes a statistical question, Linda J. Young and Megan Mocko for their article on the ASA Statistics Project competition, and Linda Quinn for her article concerning the ASA Statistics Poster competition.

Each investigation was reviewed initially by at least two reviewers. We are very thankful for their excellent comments and suggestions, which improved our writing significantly, and to Morgan Ray for her excellent work in organizing the review process. The reviewers included Debra Alcox, Judy Cain, Ruth Carver, Sharon Cichocki, Christine Franklin, Bonnie Hagelberger, Nick Horton, Christine Irons, Nathan Kidwell, Diane Loucks, Sandra McKenzie, Leigh Nataro, Jamis Perrett, Craig Refugio, Leigh Slauson, and Denise Spangler.

We extend our utmost gratitude to Rebecca Nichols, ASA director of education, who did a remarkable job producing graphs of publishable quality for BTG and providing deep dedication to and support of JC efforts. We give very special thanks to Valerie Nirala, ASA publications coordinator, whose editorial and design magic brought life to our writings, without which much of what we had to offer would have lacked reader appeal. And finally, a note of appreciation to Nick Horton, JC chair, whose leadership and direction were very much appreciated in helping us achieve our publication goals.

Pat Hopfensperger
Tim Jacobbe
Deborah Lurie
Jerry Moreno

ABOUT *BRIDGING THE GAP*

Bridging the Gap (*BTG*) consists of 20 investigations in statistics and probability for grades K–8. It is written to help teachers implement the activities in their classrooms. Each investigation consists of the following headings appropriately written for its specific content:

Overview

Learning Goals

Common Core State Standards for Mathematical Practice

Common Core State Standards Grade Level Content

NCTM *Principles and Standards for School Mathematics* (*PSSM*)

Materials

Estimated Time

Instructional Plan consisting of the four steps of the GAISE process

Example of 'Interpret the Results'

Assessment with Answers

Extensions

References

A CD-ROM is included that contains each investigation's data-collection sheets, sample tables and graphs, examples of Interpret the Results, assessment, and other material for ease of making copies for classroom use. Material on the CD-ROM is indicated by ☻ throughout the book.

There are four investigations in each of the following five topic sections:

Section 2 - Looking at Data

Section 3 - Describing Distributions

Section 4 - Comparing Groups

Section 5 - Exploring Relationship

Section 6 - Investigating Probability

GAISE Framework

The GAISE framework emphasizes hands-on learning of statistics by using four steps:

Formulating a statistical question that can be answered with data

Designing and implementing a plan to collect appropriate data

Analyzing the collected data by graphical and numerical methods

Interpreting the results of the analysis in the context of the original question

In addition to references to the various Common Core (*www.corestandards.org*) and National Council of Teachers of Mathematics' *PSSM* standards, each investigation explicitly contains the four components of the problem solving process presented in the American Statistical Association's *Guidelines for Assessment and Instruction in Statistics Education (GAISE) Report: A Pre-K–12 Curriculum Framework* (*www.amstat.org/education/gaise*). The GAISE framework emphasizes hands-on learning of statistics by using four steps: formulating a statistical question that can be answered with data; designing and implementing a plan to collect appropriate data; analyzing the collected data by graphical and numerical methods; and interpreting the results of the analysis in the context of the original question. A second component of the GAISE framework is comprised of three levels of statistical development (levels A, B, and C detailed on pages 14 and 15 of the GAISE report). Students must progress through these levels to develop statistical understanding. In this regard, it is highly recommended that Level A investigations be presented before those at Level B.

By having written these investigations in the spirit of the GAISE framework, the authors of *Bridging the Gap* intend to help teachers unpack the Common Core State Standards (CCSS) for Mathematical Practice and the CCSS Statistics and Probability Domain for grades 6–8. As students progress through grades K–5, they will build a quantitative foundation in the CCSS Measurement and Data Domain in preparation for their study of statistics that begins in earnest in grade 6. This foundation is expanded in the middle school grades' standards with the "CCSS clusters" of developing understanding of statistical variability; summarizing and describing distributions; using random sampling to draw inferences about a population; drawing informal comparative inferences about two populations; investigating chance processes and developing, using, and evaluating probability models; and investigating patterns of association in bivariate data. *Bridging the Gap* follows this progression of growth in students' understanding of statistics and probability by providing model lessons tied to the CCSS and GAISE framework.

Note that in Linking Investigations, tables have been provided on pages xv and xvi to help teachers identify the connection of each investigation to GAISE levels A and B and the Common Core State Standards across grade levels. For planning purposes, a table has been included showing estimates of the time required to complete each investigation.

A brief description of the sections follows:

Section 1: Getting Started: Step One of the Data Analysis Process is devoted to the first GAISE step, formulating a statistical question that can be answered with data. It is important that this section is covered before doing any of the other sections. Understanding what is and is not a statistical question is fundamental to the statistical process.

Section 2: Looking at Data consists of four Level A investigations with emphasis on categorical data for one variable. This is the most basic of the five topic sections and is appropriate as an introduction to statistical thinking.

Section 3: Building distributions and describing their "center, spread, shape" is fundamental to understanding statistical variability. This section, Describing Distributions, discusses in particular the mean absolute deviation (MAD), a measure of spread that will be new to many teachers (CCSS 6.SP.5c). The importance of understanding and using the MAD is not only to develop a viable measure of variability, but also one that makes the understanding of standard deviation—a highly important measure of variation learned in the high-school curriculum—much clearer.

Section 4: Comparing Groups is concerned with experimental design for two variables for both numerical and categorical variables. All four of the investigations in this section are at GAISE Level B, so students need to have seen at least one investigation from Section 2 before tackling these.

Section 5: Exploring Relationship corresponds to the CCSS for Grade 8 on investigating bivariate data. Constructing scatterplots and drawing best-fitting lines through data that exhibit a linear relationship fit well into the Grade 8 mathematics standard of developing the equation of a line.

Section 6: The GAISE framework views probability as a mathematical model and a tool for statistics. This section, Investigating Probability, develops fundamental concepts of probability that pave the way for developing probability models at the high-school level.

Section 7: Teacher resources such as articles about the ASA poster and project competitions, STatistics Education Web (STEW), Statistics Teacher Network, Census at School, and webinars are included.

Bridging the Gap is designed so each lesson can stand alone. Our goal is to provide you with a resource giving you and your students data analysis experiences that bring the standards to life. It also is designed to give you flexibility. Several investigations can be completed in one class period, but many require multiple class periods so students can collect their data. For planning purposes, the following table shows an estimate of the time required to complete each investigation. Additional time will be needed for the assessment and extensions.

Estimated Time Guide

Investigation	Estimated Time
1.1	1 day
2.1	2 days
2.2	1 day
2.3	1 day
2.4	2 days
3.1	1 day
3.2	2 days
3.3	2 days
3.4	2–3 days
4.1	1–2 days
4.2	1–2 days
4.3	2 days
4.4	1 day
5.1	1–2 days
5.2	2 days
5.3	1 day
5.4	2 days
6.1	1 day
6.2	1 day
6.3	1 day
6.4	1–2 days

LINKING INVESTIGATIONS

The following table shows the alignment of the GAISE levels A and B with the investigations in *Bridging the Gap*.

Linking GAISE Levels and Bridging the Gap

Investigation	Level A	Level B
1.1	X	X
2.1	X	
2.2	X	X
2.3	X	X
2.4	X	
3.1	X	
3.2	X	
3.3		X
3.4		X
4.1		X
4.2		X
4.3		X
4.4		X
5.1		X
5.2		X
5.3		X
5.4		X
6.1	X	
6.2	X	
6.3		X
6.4		X

The following table shows the alignment of the Common Core State Standards between the investigations in *Bridging the Gap* and grades K–8. Each investigation also is linked with the **Common Core State Standards for Mathematical Practice**. The following four practices are the focus of many of the investigations:

1. Make sense of problems and persevere in solving them.

2. Reason abstractly and quantitatively.

3. Construct viable arguments and critique the reasoning of others.

4. Model with mathematics.

Linking Grade Levels and the Common Core State Standards

Investigation	Grades K–5	Grade 6	Grade 7	Grade 8
1.1		6.SP.1		
2.1	K.MD.3, 1.MD.4, 2.MD.10			
2.2	K.MD.3, 1.MD.4, 2.MD.10			
2.3	K.MD.3, 1.MD.4, 2.MD.10			
2.4	K.MD.3, 1.MD.4, 2.MD.10			
3.1	K.CC.7			
3.2		6.SP.1-4		
3.3		6.EE.2, 6.SP.1-4		
3.4		6.SP.1-5		
4.1		6.SP.1-5		
4.2		6.SP.1-5	7.SP.3	
4.3		6.SP.1 and 5, 6.RP.1		8.SP.1
4.4		6.RP.3c, 6.SP.3		8.SP.4
5.1				8.SP.1
5.2				8.SP.1
5.3				8.SP.1 and 2
5.4				8.F.3 and 4, 8.SP.2 and 3
6.1			7.SP.5	
6.2		6.SP.1 and 2	7.SP.5 and 8a	
6.3			7.SP.5, 7.SP.7b, 7.SP.8	
6.4			7.SP.6	

GETTING STARTED

Introduction

The objective of the *Guidelines for Assessment and Instruction in Statistics Education* (*GAISE*) *Report* is to provide a conceptual framework for K–12 statistics education. The GAISE Framework outlines three statistical maturity levels—A, B, and C—that are based on experience, not on age or grade level. The framework stresses hands-on active learning and that statistical analysis is an investigative process that turns loosely formed ideas into scientific studies by doing the following:

1. Formulating a question that can be answered with data

2. Designing a plan to collect appropriate data

3. Analyzing the collected data by graphical and numerical methods

4. Interpreting the results to reflect light on the original question

The four-step statistical problem-solving process is also part of the Common Core State Standards, as found in the Grade 6 Statistics and Probability Content Standards, 6.SP.

Develop understanding of statistical variability.

6.SP.1 Recognize a statistical question as one that anticipates variability in the data related to the question and accounts for it in the answers. *Ex. "How old am I?" is not a statistical question, but "How old are the students in my school?" is a statistical question, because one anticipates variability in students' ages.*

6.SP.2 Understand that a set of data collected to answer a statistical question has a distribution, which can be described by its center, spread, and overall shape.

6.SP.3 Recognize that a measure of center for a numerical data set summarizes all of its values with a single number, while a measure of variation describes how its values vary with a single number.

Summarize and describe distributions.

6.SP.4 Display numerical data in plots on a number line, including dot plots, histograms, and box plots.

6.SP.5 Summarize numerical data sets in relation to their context, such as by the following:

a. Reporting the number of observations

b. Describing the nature of the attribute under investigation, including how it was measured and its units of measurement

c. Giving quantitative measures of center (median and/or mean) and variability (interquartile range and/or mean absolute deviation), as well as describing any overall pattern and striking deviations from the overall pattern with reference to the context in which the data were gathered

d. Relating the choice of measures of center and variability to the shape of the data distribution and context in which the data were gathered.

The purpose of the following investigation is to help your students learn how to formulate a statistical question—a question that can be answered with data.

INVESTIGATION 1.1
FORMULATING A STATISTICAL QUESTION

Overview

The GAISE report emphasizes the *process* of doing a statistical study. The first step in that process requires the investigator to formulate a question that will be the focus of the study. This investigation provides a framework for teachers to use to help their students construct questions that can be addressed through the collection and analysis of data. These types of questions are called **statistical questions**. In posing the questions, students will be encouraged to think about the **population** (subjects) to be studied, the **variable** (characteristic) to be measured, and the **variation** that may occur in the **measurement** of that characteristic.

As stated in the Common Core State Standards, a statistical question is one that "anticipates variability in the data and accounts for this variability in the analysis." The objective of this investigation is to assist students in generating statistical questions about their schools, neighborhoods, and interesting phenomena in the world and describing the type of data that would need to be collected to answer those questions.

GAISE Components

This investigation stresses the first component (formulate a question) of statistical problem solving put forth in the GAISE report. It can be used with GAISE Level A and Level B students.

Learning Goals

Students will be able to do the following after finishing this investigation:

- Distinguish statistical questions from nonstatistical questions

- Identify the population (subjects) to be studied

- Identify the data (values of a variable) to be collected

- Develop an intuitive understanding of the expected variation in the data

Common Core State Standards
for Mathematical Practice

1. Make sense of problems and persevere in solving them.
4. Model with mathematics.

Common Core State Standards
Grade Level Content

6.SP1 Recognize a statistical question as one that anticipates variability in the data related to the question and accounts for it in the answers.

NCTM Principles and Standards
for School Mathematics

Data Analysis and Probability

Grades 6–8 Formulate questions that can be addressed with data and collect, organize, and display relevant data to answer them.

Materials 💿

Statistical Questions Worksheet Level A and Level B

Estimated Time

One day

Instructional Plan

1. Begin the investigation by asking your students what they would be interested in finding out about their school, neighborhood, or families and friends. Many questions students generate will be interesting, but may not be statistical questions. Discuss with your students that a statistical question is one that can be answered with data and that **variability** in the data is expected. A well-written statistical question refers to a **population** of interest, a **measurement** of interest, and **anticipates answers that vary**.

   While the question, "How old is my math teacher?" might be of interest, it is not a statistical question because there is only a single subject, and hence no variability. "How old are the teachers in our school?" is a statistical question because "teachers in our school" is the population, "age" is the measurement variable, and we expect several ages.

> A well-written statistical question refers to a **population** of interest, a **measurement** of interest, and **anticipates answers that vary**.

Help your students understand that nonstatistical questions may be too broad or specific. The question, "Do people like pizza?" is too broad. It is unclear exactly what the population is. A better version would be, "Of all the 4th-graders in our school, who likes pepperoni pizza?" The population is "the 4th-graders in our school," the measurement is "like or don't like pepperoni pizza," and we would expect some people to like this type of pizza and some not to like it. The question, "How many words are in this sentence?" is narrow and has no variability in its answer. However, "How many words are in the sentences in this book?" is a statistical question. The population is "all the sentences in this book," the measurement is the "length of the sentences," and we would expect the sentences to be different lengths.

2. Pose the following question to your students and have them decide whether it is a statistical question. "How old is my pet dog?" This is not a statistical question because there is no variability—there is a single subject or unit, and hence no variability. Discuss with your students how this question could be rewritten into a statistical question about the class. One suggestion: "How old are the pets of the students in our class?" The population of interest is the "students' pets," the measurement is the "pets' ages," and we would expect the pets would be different ages.

3. Pose the question, "What is my favorite topping on a pizza?" Ask your students why this is not a statistical question, and ask them to rewrite it into a statistical question. Possible answer: "What do the students in this class prefer as their favorite topping on a pizza?" The population is the "students in class," the measurement is their "favorite pizza topping," and we would expect different answers such as cheese, sausage, or pepperoni.

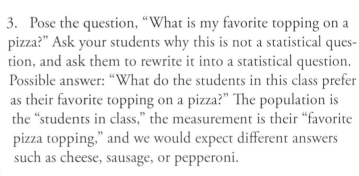

4. Place your students into groups of four. Give each group the appropriate level A or B list of questions in Table 1.1.1 or Table 1.1.2. For each question, the groups should indicate whether the question is a statistical question and give reasons for their answer. If they answer that the question is a statistical one, they should specify the population, measurement taken, and expected variation. If it is not a statistical question, they should explain why it is not a statistical question and rewrite it so it is a statistical question.

Table 1.1.1: Level A Questions

Question	Statistical Question (Y or N)	Explain Your Answer	Question	Statistical Question (Y or N)	Explain Your Answer
What colors are the shoes worn by the teachers in our school?			How many languages does my friend speak?		
What are the shapes of all the buttons on the clothes worn by the students in this class?			How far can I jump?		
How many times does the word "bridge" appear in the rhyme "London Bridge Is Falling Down"?			Does my best friend like McDonald's Happy Meals?		
How many pockets do I have?			Is my last name the longest name in class?		
What is my fifth-grade sister's favorite animal at the zoo?			What is the favorite lunch of third-graders in our school?		

Table 1.1.2: Level B Questions

Question	Statistical Question (Y or No)	Explain Your Answer	Question	Statistical Question (Y or No)	Explain Your Answer
Can I roll my tongue?			Who was the oldest U.S. president when inaugurated?		
How do the lengths of the first names of students in class compare to the lengths of their last names?			Are students in our class who are 4'5" or taller able to jump higher than students who are shorter than 4'5"?		
Am I going to win a prize at the school carnival?			Which brand of pizza has the most pepperoni?		
What is the longest-lasting brand of AA batteries?			Do plants grow better under colored lights?		
A teacher asks her class, "What is your shoe size?"			Is it easier to remember a set of objects or a list of words?		
Which brand of bubble gum holds its flavor the longest?					

5. Discuss with your students their answers to each question. Following are suggested answers.

Table 1.1.3: Suggested Answers to Level A Questions

Question	Statistical Question (Y or N)	Explain Your Answer
What colors are the shoes worn by the teachers in our school?	Y	Population is teachers in school; measurement is shoe color, data are various colors
What are the shapes of all the buttons on the clothes worn by the students in this class?	Y	Population is all the buttons worn by students in class; measurement is button shape; data are various shapes
How many times does the word "bridge" appear in the rhyme "London Bridge Is Falling Down"?	N	There is one word in the population, hence no variability—only single frequency for an answer.
What is the frequency of the words that appear in the nursery rhyme "London Bridge is Falling Down"?		Population is all words in the rhyme; measurement is number of times each appears; data are words with their frequency of occurrence
How many pockets do I have?	N	There is one person in the population, hence no variability in number of pockets I have.
How many pockets do the students in class have on the clothes they are wearing today?		Population is all students in class; measurement is number of pockets; data are 0, 1, 2, …
How many languages does my friend speak?	N	There is one person in the population, hence no variability—only one number for an answer.
How many languages do the students in my school speak?		Population is all students at my school; measurement is number of languages each student speaks; data are 1, 2, 3, …
How far can I jump?	N	There is one person in the population, hence no variability—only one distance.
How far can the students in this class jump?		Population is all students in class; measurement is distance one can jump; data are real numbers
Does my best friend like McDonald's Happy Meals?	N	There is one person in the population—my friend—so there is no variability only one answer—yes or no.
Of the fifth-graders in our school, who likes McDonald's Happy Meals?		Population is all fifth-graders in our school; measurement is yes/no liking of Happy Meals; data are a listing of students with yes or no response for each
What is my sister's favorite animal at the zoo?	N	There is one person in the population, hence no variability—only one animal name for an answer.
Which animal in the local zoo would the fifth-graders pick as their favorite?		Population is fifth-graders; measurement is favorite zoo animal; data are various animals
Is my last name the longest name in class?	N	There is one person in the population, hence there is no variability—only one answer.
How long are the last names of students in this class?		Population is class students; measurement is length of last name; data are various last names
What is the favorite lunch of third-graders in our school?	Y	Population is third-graders; measurement is the name of favorite lunch; variability—we would expect students to give answers such as pizza, sandwiches, or macaroni and cheese

Table 1.1.4: Suggested Answers to Level B Questions

Question	Statistical Question (Y or N)	Explain Your Answer
Can I roll my tongue?	N	There is one person in the population, hence there is no variability—only one answer.
How do boys and girls compare regarding the ability to roll their tongues?		Population is all boys and girls in class; measurement is whether a student can roll his/her tongue; data are yes/no for each student
How do the lengths of the first names of students in class compare to the lengths of their last names?	Y	Population is students in class; measurement is difference in length of first and last names; we would expect the differences to vary from student to student
If everyone in class plays "spin-the-wheel" at the school carnival, what are their chances of winning?	Y	Population is the students in class; measurement is win or not win; we would expect some students to win and others to not
What is the longest-lasting brand of AA batteries?	Y	Population is different brands of batteries; measurement is battery length of life; we would expect the brands to last varying lengths of time
A teacher asks her class, "What is your shoe size?"	Y	Population is implied to be all students in class; measurement is shoe size; we would expect students to have different shoe sizes
Which brand of bubble gum holds its flavor the longest?	Y	Population is brands of bubble gum; measurement is how long flavor lasts; we would expect different brands would vary on how long their flavor lasts
Who was the oldest U.S. president when inaugurated?	N	There is only one person in the population, the name of the oldest president when inaugurated, hence no variability.
How old were the U.S. presidents when they were inaugurated?		Population is all U.S. presidents; measurement is age when inaugurated; data are various ages
Are students in our class who are 4'5" or taller able to jump higher than students who are shorter than 4'5"?	Y	Population is "tall" students and "short" students in our class; measurement is how high one can jump; we would expect students to jump different heights
Which brand of pizza has the most pepperoni?	Y	Population is different brands of pizza; measurement is the count of number of pieces of pepperoni on a pizza; we would expect different brands to have different amounts of pepperoni
Do plants grow better under colored lights?	N	More specific population should be listed. Define what it means to grow better, and need to specify the colors of light.
Do tomato plants grow taller under red light, blue light, or daylight?		Population is tomato plants; measurement is height under red light, blue light, or daylight; we expect heights to vary
Is it easier to remember a set of objects or a list of words?	N	There is no population mentioned.
Are the seventh-graders able to memorize the names of a set of objects better than a list of words?		Population is all seventh-graders; measurement is number of objects recalled and number of words recalled; we expect the number of correct responses to vary

Assessment with Answers

Level A

A third-grader's favorite sport was soccer. She asked all the students in her room, "Who likes to watch a soccer game?" Explain why this is a statistical question. The population is "all the students in her room." The measurement is "whether a student likes to watch soccer." Variation is expected with some students answering "yes" and some answering "no."

Level B

A group of seventh-grade students asked the question, "What's the fastest animal in the world?"

1. Explain why this is not a statistical question. There is no variability—there is just one fastest animal.

2. Rewrite the question so it is a statistical question. How many miles per hour can various animals run?

Extension

Ask your students to choose one of the questions they have decided is a statistical question or one they have rewritten into a statistical question. Have students discuss how they might collect data to help answer the question and describe the variability in the data they might expect.

Note: Some of the questions in tables 1.1.1 and 1.1.2 will be addressed in the investigations in this book.

References

Franklin, C., G. Kader, D. Mewborn, J. Moreno, R. Peck, M. Perry, and R. Scheaffer. 2007. *Guidelines for assessment and instruction in statistics education (GAISE) report: A pre-k–12 curriculum framework*. Alexandria, VA: American Statistical Association.

National Council of Teachers of Mathematics. 2000. *Principles and standards for school mathematics*. Reston, VA: National Council of Teachers of Mathematics.

Common Core State Standards for Mathematics, www.corestandards.org.

LOOKING AT DATA

INVESTIGATION 2.1
WHAT COLORS ARE OUR SHOES?

Overview

This investigation focuses on students collecting, analyzing, and interpreting **categorical** data. Students generate questions regarding what they want to know about their shoes and then sort them according to an attribute or variable, a characteristic of a person or object that may vary from individual to individual. A **Venn diagram** is constructed to reflect the shoe sort. The shoes are then used to create a tally chart/frequency table according to the variable, and this display is used to construct a **bar graph.** The data are organized, displayed, and compared in a Venn diagram, tally chart/frequency table, and bar graph. A bar graph is the primary data display used to present categorical data.

GAISE Components

This investigation follows the four components of statistical problem solving put forth in the *Guidelines for Assessment and Instruction in Statistics Education (GAISE) Report.* The four components are formulate a statistical question that can be answered with data, design and implement a plan to collect appropriate data, analyze the collected data by graphical and numerical methods, and interpret the results of the analysis in the context of the original question. This is a GAISE Level A activity.

Learning Goals

Students will be able to do the following after finishing this investigation:

- Generate statistical questions about their shoes

- Compare and sort shoes using various attributes or variables

- Use a Venn diagram, tally chart/frequency table, and bar graph to organize and display data

- Analyze the data and record a conclusion in the context of the original question

Common Core State Standards for Mathematical Practice

1. Make sense of problems and persevere in solving them.
2. Reason abstractly and quantitatively.

3. Construct viable arguments and critique the reasoning of others.

4. Model with mathematics.

Common Core State Standards
Grade Level Content

K.MD3 Classify objects into given categories; count the numbers of objects in each category and sort the categories by count.

1.MD4 Organize, represent, and interpret data with up to three categories; ask and answer questions about the total number of data points, how many in each category, and how many more or fewer are in one category than in another.

2.MD.10 Draw a picture graph and bar graph (with single-unit scale) to represent a data set with up to four categories. Solve simple put-together, take-apart, and compare problems using information presented in a bar graph.

NCTM Principles and Standards
for School Mathematics

Data Analysis and Probability

Pre-K–2 All students should pose questions and gather data about themselves and their surroundings; sort and classify objects according to their attributes and organize data about the objects; and represent data using concrete objects, pictures, and graphs.

Materials

- Yarn or plastic hoops
- Chart paper with grids
- Paper for labels
- Pencil or marker

Estimated Time

Two days

Instructional Plan

✏ Formulate a Statistical Question

1. The president of a shoe company would like to know something about the shoes students in our class wear.

2. Ask the following question: What can we tell the president of the shoe company about our shoes?

3. Possible student responses: color, type (e.g., tennis, sandal), material (e.g., leather, canvas), sole (e.g., smooth, bumpy), laces, etc.

4. Lead your students to frame ideas into statistical questions—what type of shoes do we have? What color are our shoes? What are our shoes made of? How do we fasten our shoes?

5. Pick one attribute to explore. For example, you may choose the question, "What colors are the shoes of the students in our class?" **Note:** This statistical question will be carried through the investigation as a means of providing an example situation. As many shoes have multiple colors, students would be asked to consider only the color that is most prevalent on their shoes—the "main color."

✏ Collect Appropriate Data

1. Ask your students to take off one of their shoes and bring it to the front of the room.

2. Ask your students to sort their shoes on the floor by color (or a previously selected attribute).

3. Using the attribute, encircle each group with yarn (or a plastic hoop) while clarifying why shoes are placed within a particular group.

4. Develop and make labels (red, brown, etc., if color is the attribute) for each category (group of shoes).

5. Explain to your students that what they have is nice, but it would be hard to communicate this information to the president of the company without having him here. Ask your students how they could represent the shoes they have on the floor in a way that would be easily transferable to the president. Students should suggest that they could create a graph of what is on the floor.

Sorting and Displaying Data

Categorical data are values that have no numerical properties such as blood type, color, letter grade.

A **Venn diagram** uses circles to illustrate categories and their relationship to each other.

A **bar graph** is the primary tool used to display categorical data.

✏️ **Analyze the Data**

1. Represent the results of the shoe sort on chart paper. Title the chart "Colors of Our Shoes." Draw a circle for each category and label them with appropriate colors. Have each student put an asterisk (*) in the category that represents the color of his or her own shoe. See Figure 2.1.1 for an example in which eight students had white shoes, six had black shoes, and four had green shoes. Note that this graph is a Venn diagram with non-overlapping circles.

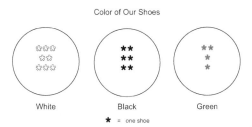

Figure 2.1.1 Venn diagram of children's shoes

2. Ask your students to compare the actual shoe sort of their shoes on the floor to the chart. How are they alike? How are they different? What does each * mean? Keep the actual shoe sort to refer to later.

3. Ask your students to explain what the Venn diagram tells them about the color of their shoes. Record their responses. For example, some responses may include the following:

   • There are not many green shoes.

   • Most of the shoes are white. (Ask them what is meant by "most." If they say "majority," then this response is not a correct one since a category would have to have more than nine to be a majority in a class of 18. A correct response would be that more students had white shoes than any other color of shoe.)

   • There are more white shoes than green shoes, and there are more white shoes than black ones.

4. Keep the Venn diagram to refer to later.

5. Tell your students the president may want to see their information in more than one way. Ask them to show the color of their shoes another way.

6. Have your students take off their other shoe. Hand out a piece of 8.5 x 11 paper to each student. The paper is to be used for constant scaling

purposes in a new graph. Note that if your students were to line up their shoes heel to toe by color and compare the heights of the lines of shoes, it is possible that three shoes in one line would be longer than three shoes in another line. Using the paper is an attempt to keep your students from making this graphical error.

7. Tell your students they are going to construct a picture graph using the paper and their shoes. At another spot on the floor, label the color categories. Be sure you have room to put all the paper from your students above the respective categories. In this example, the maximum number of shoes of one color is eight, so you need to have enough room to place eight pieces of paper in a column.

8. Have each student put his or her shoe on top of their piece of paper and place the paper with their shoe on top above the appropriate color label. The pieces of paper within a color need to line up with no space between the pieces. The result is a picture graph. See Figure 2.1.2.

Figure 2.1.2 Picture graph of children's shoes

9. Ask your students the following questions regarding the picture graph:

   a. What is the most common shoe color? Why?

   b. What is the least common shoe color? Why?

   c. How many more black shoes are there than green shoes? Explain.

10. Ask your students which graph (the Venn diagram or the picture graph) made it easier to answer these types of questions? Why did one make it easier than the other? Students should realize the picture graph is easier to use to answer these types of questions. It is especially easier for questions like "How many more …," since one can either subtract or simply "count on" to get up to the other category.

11. Remind your students that we want to write a letter to the president of the shoe company. Ask them if they will be able to send the president their picture graph. Suggest that a tally chart/frequency table is a way to summarize the picture graph. Demonstrate its construction by labeling columns on chart paper - Color, Tally, Frequency. Table 2.1.1 shows an example.

Table 2.1.1 Tally Chart/Frequency Table of Children's Shoes

Color	Tally	Frequency
White	‭𝍩‬ |||	8
Black	𝍩		6
Green	||||	4

12. Compare the tally chart/frequency table to the Venn diagram and picture graph on the floor. How are they alike? How are they different? Ask your students which display—the frequency table or the picture graph on the floor—is easier to use/read. Responses will no doubt vary, but pictures often are easier to interpret than tables.

13. Tell your students that a graph called a bar graph can be constructed from the tally chart/frequency table. Show your students how to construct a bar graph by placing categories on the horizontal axis and frequency on the vertical axis. Figure 2.1.3 shows an example of a bar graph for the above data.

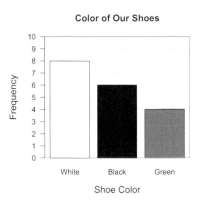

Figure 2.1.3 Bar graph of children's shoes

14. Looking at all four data displays (Venn diagram, picture graph, tally chart/frequency table, bar graph), ask your students which display helps them answer questions involving how many more/how many fewer and why? This will lead to a comparison of the data displays.

15. Ask your students which display they would prefer to use if they were to choose one to communicate the results to the president. Why?

16. Tell your students that the type of data displays used are often chosen based on the type of data and the questions to be answered by that data. Note that Venn diagrams, tally chart/frequency tables, bar graphs, and pie charts are the types of graphs for categorical data.

✐ Interpret the Results in the Context of the Original Question

1. Ask your students to write a letter to the president of the shoe company communicating their response to the president's inquiry based on their statistical question, "What colors are the shoes of the students in our class?" They should include what their data were, what analysis they did, and what conclusion they made.

2. Ask your students the following questions:

   • If we did a similar investigation across the hall, do you think we would get similar results?

   • If you live in a climate that is different from ours, do you think the color results would differ from ours?

Example of 'Interpret the Results'

Note: The following is not an example of actual student work, but an example of all the parts that should be included in student work.

Dear Shoe Company President,

You asked us to tell you something about the shoes we wear. We decided to collect data and analyze the color of our shoes. We counted the number of shoes of each color and represented our findings in the bar chart below. We chose a bar chart because we thought the heights of the bars showed the comparison of the colors the best.

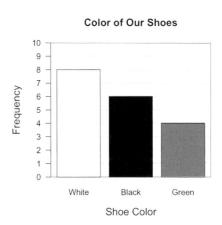

There were only three colors of shoes in our class: black, white, and green. There were eight of us who had white shoes, six who had black shoes, and four who had green. There were more white shoes than black or green, so we would recommend you concentrate on making white shoes. Actually, we want to continue our study and see if our classmates across the hall agree with our distribution of colors. We will let you know.

Also, we want to help you by looking at something other than color, like the type of shoes we wear. Many of us wear an athletic shoe, but there are other types, too.

We hope our data analysis helps you.
Thank you for asking us.

Mrs. Franklin's Class

Assessment with Answers

1. Suppose the color of shoes for a class of 20 students was as follows. W stands for white, B for black, and G for green.

G G B W W W B G W B B B W W W G B G W W

Construct two data displays for these data. Choose one of your data displays and write a letter to the president of a shoe company describing what your chosen display tells you about the color of shoes for that class. Include in your letter to the president why you chose a certain data display.

Possible displays:

Color	Tally	Frequency
Black	𝄃𝄃𝄃𝄃𝄃 𝄃	6
Green	𝄃𝄃𝄃𝄃𝄃	5
White	𝄃𝄃𝄃𝄃𝄃 𝄃𝄃𝄃𝄃	9

Tally Chart

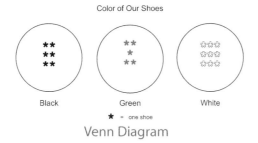

Venn Diagram

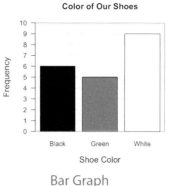

Bar Graph

Extension

Have your students collect data from another class. Using this data set, have your students construct a frequency table and a bar graph. Then, compare the results of the other class's data with your class's data. Have your students compare and contrast the bar graphs and focus on questions such as "Who has more white shoes?" "How many more?" "How many red shoes are in both classes?"

References

Franklin, C., G. Kader, D. Mewborn, J. Moreno, R. Peck, M. Perry, and R. Scheaffer. 2007. *Guidelines for assessment and instruction in statistics education (GAISE) report: A pre-k–12 curriculum framework*. Alexandria, VA: American Statistical Association. *www.amstat.org/education/gaise*.

Greenes, C. E. (ed.) 2002. *Navigating through data analysis and probability in prekindergarten – grade 2*. Reston, VA: National Council of Teachers of Mathematics.

National Council of Teachers of Mathematics. 2000. *Principles and standards for school mathematics*. Reston, VA: National Council of Teachers of Mathematics.

Common Core State Standards for Mathematics. www.corestandards.org.

INVESTIGATION 2.2
WHAT SHAPES ARE OUR BUTTONS?

Overview

This investigation focuses on students collecting, analyzing, and interpreting **categorical** data. After listening to the story "A Lost Button" in *Frog and Toad are Friends* by Arnold Lobel, students generate questions about what they want to know about buttons. Buttons are then sorted according to an attribute/variable and used to create a **tally chart/frequency table**. This display is used to construct a **bar graph**. A bar graph is the primary tool used to display categorical data.

GAISE Components

This investigation follows the four components of statistical problem solving put forth in the *Guidelines for Assessment and Instruction in Statistics Education (GAISE) Report.* The four components are formulate a statistical question that can be answered with data, design and implement a plan to collect appropriate data, analyze the collected data by graphical and numerical methods, and interpret the results of the analysis in the context of the original question. This is a GAISE Level A activity with extensions to Level B.

Learning Goals

Students will be able to do the following after finishing this investigation:

- Recognize, compare, and sort buttons using various attributes or variables

- Students will be able to use a tally chart/frequency table and a bar graph to organize and display data

- Students will be able to analyze the data and record observations

Common Core State Standards for Mathematical Practice

1. Make sense of problems and persevere in solving them.
2. Reason abstractly and quantitatively.
3. Construct viable arguments and critique the reasoning of others.
4. Model with mathematics.

Common Core State Standards
Grade Level Content

K.MD.3 Classify objects into given categories; count the numbers of objects in each category and sort the categories by count

1.MD.4 Organize, represent, and interpret data with up to three categories; ask and answer questions about the total number of data points, how many in each category, and how many more or fewer are in one category than in another

2.MD.10 Draw a picture graph and a bar graph (with single-unit scale) to represent a data set with up to four categories; solve simple put-together, take-apart, and compare problems using information presented in a bar graph.

NCTM Principles and Standards
for School Mathematics

Data Analysis and Probability

Pre-K–2 Pose questions and gather data about themselves and their surroundings; sort and classify objects according to their attributes and organize data about the objects; represent data using concrete objects, pictures, and graphs

3–5 Represent data using tables and graphs such as bar graphs

Materials

- Buttons of different sizes and shapes
- Chart paper with grids
- *Frog and Toad Are Friends* by Arnold Lobel

Estimated Time

One day

Instructional Plan

✏ **Formulate a Statistical Question**

1. Read "A Lost Button" in *Frog and Toad Are Friends* by Arnold Lobel. In this story, Toad loses a button while he and his friend, Frog, are out for a

walk. Together, Frog and Toad set out to find the button. As they search for the lost big, white, thick, and round button with four holes, they find many other buttons along the way. Toad then uses all the other buttons to decorate a new jacket for Frog.

2. Reread the story and write all the attributes of the button Toad lost on the board.

3. Ask your students how many have lost something they really like? How many have lost a button like Toad did?

4. Ask your students what they would like to know about the buttons on their clothes. Possible responses: size, color, shape, number of holes, and thickness.

5. Write their responses in the form of a question: How many holes are in our buttons? What color are our buttons? What shape are our buttons?

6. With the help of your students, decide that a statistical question to focus on is "What shape are our buttons?"

✏ Collect Appropriate Data

1. Ask your students to look at the shape of the buttons on their clothes. Students should report the shapes of their buttons. Some children may have two or three shapes. Record the shapes in a tally chart as shown in Table 2.2.1. If a student has a button that is not round or square, record their shape under the category "Other."

Note: If your students' clothes have snaps, Velcro, and elastic rather than buttons, you will have to provide a collection of buttons for them to use.

Table 2.2.1 Tally Chart of Button Shapes 💿

Shape	Tally
Round	
Square	
Other	

2. Add a column to the tally chart that shows the total number for each type of shape. This forms a tally chart/frequency table. An example is shown in table 2.2.2.

Table 2.2.2 Count/Frequency Table of Button Shapes

Shape	Tally	Count/Frequency
Round	卌 卌 |||	13
Square	卌		6
Other	||||	4

✏ **Analyze the Data**

1. Use the tally chart/frequency table to construct a bar graph to represent each button shape. Note: Place categories (round, square, other) on the horizontal axis and frequencies on the vertical axis. Figure 2.2.1 is an example of a bar graph.

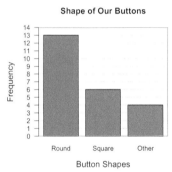

Figure 2.2.1 Bar graph of button shapes

2. Ask your students, "What is the most common button shape in our class?" (The shape "round" is called the **mode** because there were more buttons with a round shape than "square" or "other.") Which button shape occurred the least? Ask how many more buttons there were of one type as compared to another.

3. Ask how many students have the same shape as the button Toad lost (round)?

✏ **Interpret the Results in the Context of the Original Question**

1. Have your students recall the original statistical question, "What shape are our buttons?" Have students write a summary answering this question based on what they found out about the button shapes on their clothes.

2. Ask your students if they think their parents or grandparents would have the same button shapes.

Example of 'Interpret the Results'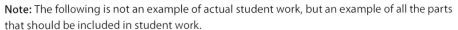

Note: The following is not an example of actual student work, but an example of all the parts that should be included in student work.

Our class read the story "A Lost Button," in which Toad loses a button that can be described by five attributes: size, color, thickness, shape, and number of holes. His button was big, white, thick, round, and had four holes. We decided to ask a statistical question for ourselves, "What shape are our buttons?" It turned out that not all of us had buttons, and some of us had more than one shape. We counted all of them. We put a tally mark for each and then counted them as frequencies in the following table.

Shape	Tally	Count/Frequency
Round	ЖЖ III	13
Square	Ж I	6
Other	IIII	4

Then, to see the results better, we drew the graph below, called a bar graph.

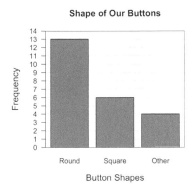

Shape of Our Buttons

From the bar graph, it is easy to see that there were more round buttons than the other shapes. Round is called the mode shape for our data. Also, we noticed that 13 of the buttons were like the shape of the one Toad lost—round. In addition to our own buttons, we are going to ask our parents and grandparents what shape of buttons they usually wear. Their mode might be different than ours. Doing this activity was a lot of fun. Another analysis we want to do is to look at one of the other attributes, such as number of holes, to see if we match Toad's four holes.

Assessment with Answers

A group of students recorded the type of buttons they had on their clothes. Table 2.2.3 shows the tallies of the type of buttons.

Table 2.2.3 Tally Chart of Button Shapes

Shape	Tally
Triangle	|||
Round	‖‖ ||
Square	‖‖ ‖‖	
Other	||

1. Which button shape is the most common? The most common button shape is square, since it occurred 11 times. Square button is the mode of this data set.

2. How many more square buttons are there than triangle buttons? There are 11 – 3 = 8 more square buttons that there are triangle buttons.

3. Make a bar graph of the different button shapes.

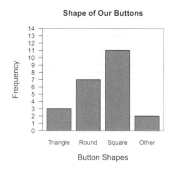

4. Write a report that indicates how the bar graph for this group of students' button shapes differs from your bar graph. Answers will vary, but students should focus on the shape of buttons and the number of each shape of button.

Level B Extension

1. Sort the buttons according to two attributes, such as shape and number of holes. Collect the data in a table similar to Table 2.2.4.

Table 2.2.4 Data-Collecting Table

	Fewer Than 3 Holes	3 Holes	4 Holes	More Than 4 Holes
Round				
Square				
Other				

2. Have your students make a bar graph of the data.

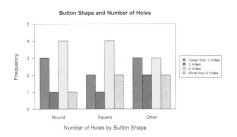 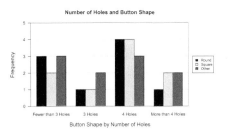

3. Ask how many students had a button like the one Toad lost (round with four holes).

References

Franklin, C., G. Kader, D. Mewborn, J. Moreno, R. Peck, M. Perry, and R. Scheaffer. 2007. *Guidelines for assessment and instruction in statistics education (GAISE) report: A pre-k–12 curriculum framework*. Alexandria, VA: American Statistical Association. *www.amstat.org/education/gaise*.

Greenes, C. E. (ed.) 2002. *Navigating through data analysis and probability in prekindergarten – grade 2*. Reston, VA: National Council of Teachers of Mathematics.

Lobel, A. 1979. *Frog and toad are friends*. New York, NY: HarperCollins.

National Council of Teachers of Mathematics. 2000. *Principles and standards for school mathematics*. Reston, VA: National Council of Teachers of Mathematics.

Common Core State Standards for Mathematics. www.corestandards.org.

INVESTIGATION 2.3
IS LONDON BRIDGE FALLING DOWN?

Overview

This investigation focuses on students building a frequency table of words from the nursery rhyme "London Bridge Is Falling Down." Students then display the data from the table on a **bar graph**. They use the table and graph to analyze and draw conclusions about the words in the poem.

GAISE Components

This investigation follows the four components of statistical problem solving put forth in the *Guidelines for Assessment and Instruction in Statistics Education (GAISE) Report.* The four components are formulate a statistical question that can be answered with data, design and implement a plan to collect appropriate data, analyze the collected data by graphical and numerical methods, and interpret the results of the analysis in the context of the original question. This is a GAISE Level A activity with extensions to Level B.

Learning Goals

Students will be able to do the following after completing this investigation:

- Generate questions about the frequency of words in a poem
- Collect data and record their observations
- Organize data in a frequency table
- Display data from a table in a bar graph
- Use the information in a frequency table and graphical display to answer formulated questions

Common Core State Standards for Mathematical Practice

1. Make sense of problems and persevere in solving them.
2. Reason abstractly and quantitatively.
3. Construct viable arguments and critique the reasoning of others.
4. Model with mathematics.

Common Core State Standards
Grade Level Content

K.MD.3 Classify objects into given categories; count the number of objects in each category, and sort the categories by count.

1.MD.4 Organize, represent, and interpret data with up to three categories; ask and answer questions about the total number of data points, how many are in each category, and how many more or fewer are in one category than in another.

2.MD.10 Draw a picture graph and bar graph (with single-unit scale) to represent a data set with up to four categories; solve simple put-together, take-apart, and compare problems using information presented in a bar graph.

NCTM Principles and Standards
for School Mathematics

Data Analysis and Probability

Pre-K–2 All students should pose questions and gather data about themselves and their surroundings and represent data using concrete objects, pictures, and graphs.

Materials

- Chart paper with the words to the rhyme "London Bridge Is Falling Down"
- Chart paper with the words found in the poem written vertically
- Grid paper

Estimated Time

One day

Instructional Plan

✏ **Formulate a Statistical Question**

1. Display the nursery rhyme "London Bridge Is Falling Down," available on the CD.

2. Have your students sing the song.

'London Bridge Is Falling Down'

London Bridge is
falling down,
Falling down, falling
down,
London Bridge is
falling down,
My fair Lady.

Build it up with wood
and clay,
Wood and clay, wood
and clay,
Build it up with wood
and clay,
My fair Lady.

Wood and clay will
wash away,
Wash away, wash
away,
Wood and clay will
wash away,
My fair Lady.

3. Discuss the history of the bridge and the rhyme with your students.

> London Bridge is a bridge over the River Thames in the city of London, England. The earliest appearance of the rhyme was in a play from the year 1659. The earliest printed English version dates from 1744 and is found in Tommy Thumb's Pretty Song Book.

4. Ask your students what they observed about the words in the song. Some of the discussion might focus on questions such as "Are there repeated words in the London Bridge nursery rhyme?" "How often do they appear?" "Unique words?" "Short words?" "How short?" "Long words?"

5. With the help of your students, decide that a statistical question to focus on is "How often do the words in the London Bridge nursery rhyme appear?"

✏ Collect Appropriate Data

1. Display a chart of the words.

2. Have your students tally how many times each word appears in the song. Record the tallies.

3. After your students have tallied the number of times each word occurs in the song, have them complete the frequency column in a tally chart/frequency table such as Table 2.3.1.

Table 2.3.1 Tally Chart for Words in 'London Bridge Is Falling Down'

Word	Tally	Count/Frequency	Word	Tally	Count/Frequency
London	||	2	It	||	2
Bridge	||	2	Up	||	2
Is	||	2	With	||	2
Falling	||||	4	Wood	ЖＩ	6
Down	||||	4	And	ЖＩ	6
My	|||	3	Clay	ЖＩ	6
Fair	|||	3	Will	||	2
Lady	|||	3	Wash	||||	4
Build	||	2	Away	||||	4

✏ Analyze the Data

1. Ask your students to use the tally chart and frequency table to answer the following questions:

   • How many words are actually in the poem? How can you use the table to find the answer?

   • How many different words are in the poem? How can you use the table to answer the question?

   • Which word or words appear most often? The word appearing most often is called the **mode**. How many times? Note that there could be more than one mode. In this example, there are three modes: "wood," "and," and "clay."

   • Which word or words appears least often? How many times?

   • Which words appear more than five times?

   • How many more times does the word "wood" appear than the word "bridge"?

   • How many words occur more than twice? Fewer than twice?

   • Where are the most-repeated words positioned in the rhyme?

2. Discuss with your students that a picture often helps answer questions. Use the frequency table to construct a bar graph as shown in Figure 2.3.1 with the words of the rhyme written horizontally and a dot above each word according to the frequency of the word. Answer the previous questions using the bar graph and ask your students which questions were easier to answer using the graph.

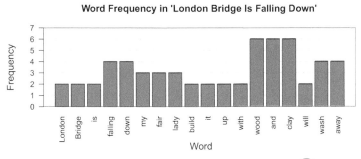

Figure 2.3.1 Bar graph of the word frequency

✏ Interpret the Results in the Context of the Original Question

1. To help interpret the data further, construct a bar graph with the words listed in order of frequency as shown in Figure 2.3.2.

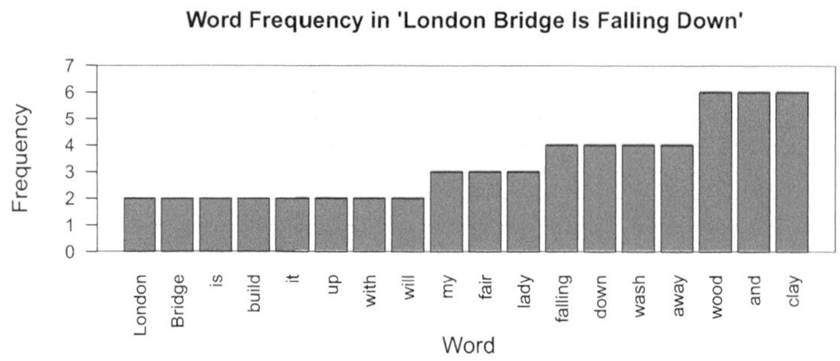

Word Frequency in 'London Bridge Is Falling Down'

Figure 2.3.2 Bar graph of the word frequency ordered 💿

2. Ask your students how this graph would help them answer the original statistical question, "How often do the words in the London Bridge nursery rhyme appear?"

3. Have them answer the statistical question by writing a report about how often the words in London Bridge appear.

4. Ask your students if they think other nursery rhymes repeat words such as they are in "London Bridge Is Falling Down?" Have your students share their answers.

Example of 'Interpret the Results' 💿

Note: The following is not an example of actual student work, but an example of all the parts that should be included in student work.

In our history class, we were studying the origins of various literary pieces including nursery rhymes. Some of us wondered what we could do with these rhymes in our mathematics class. Since we have been studying frequency tables and bar graphs there, we thought about doing a statistical analysis of a nursery rhyme. Our teacher suggested "London Bridge Is Falling Down." The statistical question we came up with was "How often do the words in the London Bridge nursery rhyme appear?" We made a tally chart listing all the words and then put a tally beside each word as we sang the rhyme slowly. Then, we counted the number of tallies and made a frequency table as follows:

London	Bridge	is	falling	down	my	fair	lady	build
2	2	2	4	4	3	3	3	2
it	up	with	wood	and	clay	will	wash	away
2	2	2	6	6	6	2	4	4

Sometimes, it's easier to make conclusions by looking at a picture, so we made a bar graph. Our teacher said that was okay as long as we kept the right vertical spacing for the counts. Here it is:

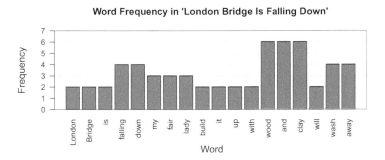

She suggested it might be even easier to discuss our question if we put the data in order.

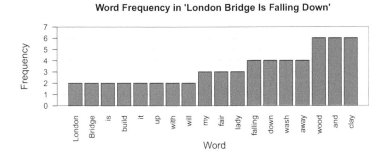

Our teacher was right, because it is clear that the words that occur most often—six times each—are "wood," "and," and "clay." All of them are modes. We also see that the mode words occurred four more times each than did the eight words that only occurred twice each (6 – 2). Now, we are wondering if there are any nursery rhymes that have unique words, since it looks like nursery rhymes like to repeat words. That will be one of our next data analysis studies.

Assessment with Answers

1. Use the nursery rhyme "Jack Be Nimble" and complete the tally chart and frequency table.

> **Jack, be nimble,**
> **Jack, be quick,**
> **Jack, jump over the candlestick.**
> **Jack, be nimble,**
> **Jack, be quick,**
> **Jack, jump over the candlestick!**

Word	Tally	Frequency
Jack	〴 l	6
Be	llll	4
Nimble	ll	2
Quick	ll	2
Jump	ll	2
Over	ll	2
The	ll	2
Candlestick	ll	2

2. Use the tally chart and frequency table to make a bar graph of the word count for the rhyme "Jack Be Nimble."

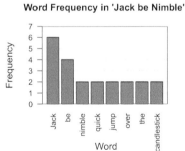

3. Use the tally chart and frequency table or the graph to answer the following questions:

    a. How many words are actually in the rhyme? How can you use the table to find the answer? There are 22 words, which were found by summing the frequencies.

50

b. How many different (distinct) words are in the rhyme? How can you use the table to answer the question? There are eight words that differ from each other. They are listed in the Word column.

c. Which word or words appear most often? How many times? "Jack" appears six times. "Jack" is the mode.

d. Which word or words appear least often? How many times? "Nimble," "Quick," "Jump," "Over," "the," and "Candlestick" each appears twice.

e. Which words appear more than three times? "Jack" appears six times and "Be" occurs four times.

f. How many more times does the word "Jack" appear than the word "jump"? "Jack" appears six times and "jump" appears twice. So "Jack" appears four more times than does "jump" (6 − 2).

Extensions

Level A Extension

Ask your students to investigate the question, "How often do the letters of the alphabet occur in the poem "London Bridge Is Falling Down?" Students can create a tally chart and frequency table using the letters of the alphabet.

Letter	Tally	Frequency
a		
b		
c		
etc.		

After your students have completed the frequency table, ask them the following questions:

Which letter or letters appear most often? Why do you think this letter appeared most often?

Which letter or letters appears least often? Why do you think this letter appeared least often?

How many more times does the letter "a" appear than the letter "m"?

To extend this activity to beginning Level B students, use the "rap" song below (available on the CD), written by the students of Sandra McKenzie, a seventh-grade teacher from Denver, Colorado.

London Bridge is falling down,
Whatcha gonna do when you go to town?
I say, London Bridge is falling down.
Hold on there, pretty lady.

Gonna build the bridge up with bricks and clay
Gotta get across, can't take all day!
Build up that bridge with bricks and clay.
Wait right there, pretty lady.
Dangerous to cross right now,
Can't 'llow no one to be goin' down.
Take the key, can't cross right now,
Chill out now, pretty lady.

Students could investigate the question, "What is the average length of the words of the 'rap' song?"

References

Franklin, C., G. Kader, D. Mewborn, J. Moreno, R. Peck, M. Perry, and R. Scheaffer. 2007. *Guidelines for assessment and instruction in statistics education (GAISE) report: A pre-k–12 curriculum framework*. Alexandria, VA: American Statistical Association. *www.amstat.org/education/gaise*.

Greenes, C. E. (ed.) 2002. *Navigating through data analysis and probability in prekindergarten – grade 2*. Reston, VA: National Council of Teachers of Mathematics.

National Council of Teachers of Mathematics. 2000. *Principles and standards for school mathematics*. Reston, VA: National Council of Teachers of Mathematics.

Common Core State Standards for Mathematics. www.corestandards.org.

INVESTIGATION 2.4
HOW CAN WE SORT OUR JUNK?

Overview

This investigation introduces students to the idea of an **attribute** or **variable**, a characteristic of a person or object that may vary from individual to individual. Using actual objects, students will organize them by an attribute and create a graphical display. Students will then verbally describe interesting patterns about the attribute using such terms as most common values (categories), least common values, many values (lots of variation), and few values (minimal variation). By the end of the activity, students will be able to identify attributes, display the **distribution** of their possible values in a graph, answer questions about the occurrence of different values of the attribute, and begin to grasp the concept of variability.

GAISE Components

This investigation follows the four components of statistical problem solving put forth in the *Guidelines for Assessment and Instruction in Statistics Education (GAISE) Report*. The four components are formulate a statistical question that can be answered with data, design and implement a plan to collect appropriate data, analyze the collected data by graphical and numerical methods, and interpret the results of the analysis in the context of the original question. This is a GAISE Level A activity.

Learning Goals

Students will be able to do the following after finishing this investigation:

- Identify an attribute or variable pertaining to an object

- Organize information about an attribute using a graphical display

- Describe the patterns (distribution of values) illustrated in the graphs

- Develop a sense for the amount of variation that may exist in the attribute

Common Core State Standards for Mathematical Practice

1. Make sense of problems and persevere in solving them.
2. Reason abstractly and quantitatively.

3. Construct viable arguments and critique the reasoning of others.
4. Model with mathematics.

Common Core State Standards
Grade Level Content

K.MD3 Classify objects into given categories; count the numbers of objects in each category and sort the categories by count.

1.MD4 Organize, represent, and interpret data with up to three categories; ask and answer questions about the total number of data points, how many in each category, and how many more or fewer are in one category than in another.

2.MD.10 Draw a picture graph and a bar graph (with single-unit scale) to represent a data set with up to four categories. Solve simple put-together, take-apart, and compare problems using information presented in a bar graph.

NCTM Principles and Standards
for School Mathematics

Data Analysis and Probability

Pre-K–2 All students should pose questions and gather data about themselves and their surroundings; sort and classify objects according to their attributes and organize data about the objects; and represent data using concrete objects, pictures, and graphs.

Materials

- Chart paper with 1" square grid

- Pencil or marker

- Bags with assorted objects (e.g., beads, buttons, charms, cubes, attribute blocks, fabric swatches, crayons, catalog pictures of jewelry, clothes) **Note:** You will need one bag for each group of four students

Estimated Time

Two days

Instructional Plan

✏️ **Formulate a Statistical Question**

1. Begin this investigation showing your students a bag of 'junk' (e.g., a bag containing beads, buttons, charms, cubes, attribute blocks, fabric swatches, crayons, catalog pictures of jewelry, clothes). Tell your students this bag of junk is material you have collected or have left over from projects or class activities. Ask them if they have a junk drawer at home. What do they have in their drawer? Ask your students what they think might be in your bag.

2. Empty the bag and tell your students you would like to organize the materials to describe what has been accumulated over the years. Ask your students to suggest some ways they could help you sort your things. Possible student responses: type (toy, button, bead, block), color, size (large, small), design (solid, striped, plaid).

> An **attribute,** or **variable,** is a characteristic of a person or object that may vary from individual to individual.

3. Lead students to frame ideas into questions. What kind of objects do we have? For a specific type of object, what attribute should we use as a sorting factor? Possible attributes include color, size, texture, etc. How will the choice of attribute affect the outcome of the sorting process?

4. This investigation assumes beads are the junk of interest. It focuses on analyzing two statistical questions: Do our beads differ in color? Do our beads differ in shape?

✏️ **Collect Appropriate Data**

1. Have your students work in groups of four.

2. Give each group a bag of 'junk' that contains different objects such as buttons, marbles, beads, etc. Tell them to look in their bag of materials and select objects to sort, along with an attribute or characteristic by which to sort them. Have the students in each group discuss possible attributes that can be used. Encourage them to consider different ways to sort their junk. (In this investigation, beads have been chosen to sort according to their color and according to their shape.)

3. Allow your students time to explore and discuss the objects as they sort them. Once they have decided how they will sort the objects, assist them in completing the data collection sheet (available on the CD). As they place the objects on the data collection sheet, they should place one

object in each section under the proper heading. Figures 2.4.1 and 2.4.2 show examples of a completed data collection sheet for sorting beads by color and shape.

4. Have each group share their findings with the class.

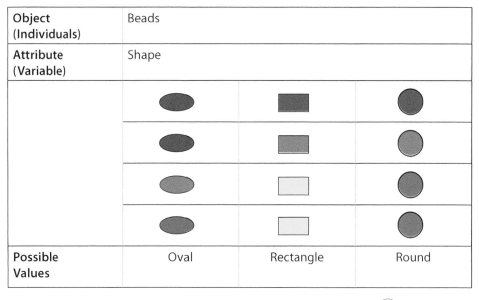

Object (Individuals)	Beads			
Attribute (Variable)	Color			
	⬭			
	⬭	⬭		🔵
	▭	🔵	▭	🔵
	🔵	▭	▭	⬭
Possible Values	Red	Blue	Yellow	Green

Figure 2.4.1 Data collection sheet for attribute of color

Object (Individuals)	Beads		
Attribute (Variable)	Shape		
	⬭	▭	🔵
	⬭	▭	🔵
	⬭	▭	🔵
	⬭	▭	🔵
Possible Values	Oval	Rectangle	Round

Figure 2.4.2 Data collection sheet for attribute of shape

✏️ **Analyze the Data**

1. Tell your students you would like a way to display their data collection sheet on the bulletin board. One way to display their data collection sheet is to make a pictograph.

2. Hand out grid paper with 1" squares. Ask each group to create a pictograph of their physical graph that they can post on the bulletin board to share with the class. This graph is made by having your students draw a picture of their data collection. Figure 2.4.3 shows an example of a pictograph based on the attribute of color.

Beads Sorted by Color			
🔴			
🔴	🟦		🟢
🟥	⚫	⬜	⚫
⚫	🔵	⬜	⚫
Red	**Blue**	**Yellow**	**Green**

Figure 2.4.3 Pictograph of the beads sorted by color

3. Another option for displaying the data collection sheet is to make a bar graph. Hand out another sheet of grid paper. Show your students how to make a bar graph from their pictographs. Place the categories (red, blue, yellow, green in this example) on the horizontal axis and count on the vertical axis. Figure 2.4.4 is an example of a bar graph based on the example of the beads sorted by color.

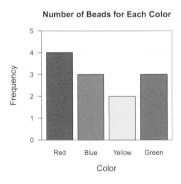

Figure 2.4.4 Bar graph of the beads sorted by color

4. Ask the students in each group to discuss each of the following questions:

   a. What sorting factor was used (e.g., color, size, shape, use, material used for construction)?

   b. What categories were used for this attribute?

   c. Of which category do you have the most? The least? Equal amounts? Record the students' responses.

✏ Interpret the Results in the Context of the Original Question

1. Have each group share their displays, and share the answers to the questions. As each group presents their displays, ask them the following questions:

   a. What other attributes did your group discuss? Why did your group choose this attribute?

   b. How did you determine the categories for your attribute? For example, what would change if instead of using the actual color of the object, we consider the categories "red" and "not red"?

2. After all the groups have presented, ask which groups used the same attribute to sort their "junk." For the groups that used the same attribute, compare the groups' displays. Are they similar? How are they different?

3. Have your students recall that the original question was, "How can we sort our junk?" Have your students write a summary of their analysis, including how they displayed their data, what graph(s) they created, and what they learned from the investigation regarding the type of junk they have by the process of sorting.

Example of 'Interpret the Results'

Note: The following is not an example of actual student work, but an example of all the parts that should be included in student work.

Our teacher asked us if we collected junk. Most of us said we do. He then asked if we had any sort of preference for one characteristic of our junk over another, like color, size, or design. We never really thought about it in that way, so he brought in a bag of "junk" he had collected from doing class activities over a long time. Our problem was to investigate the question, "How can we sort his bag of junk?" We decided to just look at the 12 beads in the bag and sorted the actual beads on two pieces of grid paper, one with regard to color and the other with regard to shape.

We chose color just because we like color, but we chose shape because we have been looking at different shapes in our geometry class. Then, we drew a pictograph to show graphs of how we sorted the beads. We used graph paper to keep our rows the same so the same number of beads—regardless of their shape—took up the same amount of vertical space. Another group in class drew a bar graph. They didn't have to make sure the same number of beads for different colors took up the same amount of space because the rectangles do that automatically. So maybe it's easier to draw a bar graph, but we liked the pictographs because we can see the beads.

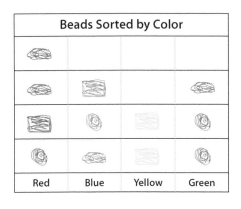

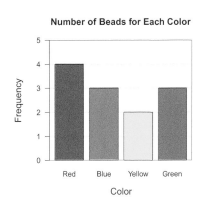

We can see from either graph that the mode color is red, but if we wanted to compare red to non-red, then the mode would be non-red, since there would be eight of them compared to the four red.

When we sorted by shape, the graphs looked different from the color graphs. The shape graphs only have three columns because there are three shapes: oval, rectangle, and round. Also, the heights were all equal because there were four beads in each shape category. That means there was the same number of each shape.

Beads Sorted by Shape		
🫘	▭	◎
🫘	▭	◎
🫘	▭	◎
🫘	▭	◎
Oval	Rectangle	Round

Assessment with Answers

Give each of your students the following pattern blocks: 6 Yellow Hexagons, 4 Green Triangles, 3 Red Trapezoids, 2 Blue Parallelograms, and 2 Tan Parallelograms. Instruct your students to sort the shapes and complete the following questions:

1. How did you decide to sort the shapes? Students can sort by color or the number of sides.

2. Draw a pictograph of how you sorted the shapes.

Shapes Sorted by Color				
⬡				
⬡				
⬡			▲	
⬡	⬛		▲	
⬡	⬛	▱	▲	◇
⬡	⬛	▱	▲	◇
Yellow	Red	Blue	Green	Tan

Shapes Sorted by # of Sides			
	◇		
	◇		⬡
	▱		⬡
▲	▱		⬡
▲	⬛		⬡
▲	⬛		⬡
▲	⬛		⬡
3	4	5	6

3. Which category had the most shapes? If they sorted by color, yellow has the most shapes. If they sorted by number of sides, then there are seven shapes with four sides.

4. Which category had the fewest shapes? If they sorted by color, the blue and tan shapes each have two. If they sorted by number of sides, then there are four shapes with three sides.

Extension

1. Have students select another set of objects and attribute and repeat the exercise. Ask them to comment on how this display differs from the one done in class. Have them write a summary of their investigation to another group. The note should address the following points:

   a. Was the sorting attribute clearly identified?

   b. Was the display easy to interpret?

   c. Was the information displayed in a clever fashion?

   d. Can you make any suggestions for improving the display?

   e. Did you learn ways to improve your graphical display?

2. Play "Gatekeeper." All students hold an attribute block and stand in line. Participants file past the gatekeeper, who has one attribute in mind. The participants are admitted with a "yes" response if their attribute matches the sorting factor in the mind of the gatekeeper (for example, all squares). Others are turned away with a "no," because they don't have the correct sorting factor. The group then identifies the sorting factor used by the gatekeeper when all participants have filed past.

3. Extend the game with two gatekeepers. If a participant gets through the first gatekeeper, they encounter the second one (for example, all yellow). Similarly, as with the first gatekeeper, the participant either gets to pass through or not. Note that those who pass through now possess two common attributes. (In this case, they are both square and yellow.)

4. After playing "Gatekeeper," have your students collect, organize, and display the data. In the one-attribute case, a possible graph would be a bar graph with the horizontal axis labeled "yes" or "no." Have your students suggest other ways to represent the data. In the two-attribute case, Venn diagrams work well with one circle labeled "square," the other "yellow."

The overlapping part would contain the yellow squares. Your students' attribute blocks could be placed physically on a large Venn diagram or represented by dots, say, on a smaller one.

5. Use this kind of activity in other subject areas.

    a. Classify rocks, leaves, shells, and so on, as an extension of a science topic.

    b. Sort letters of the alphabet or words in a poem according to similarity in language arts.

    c. Provide a U.S. map to groups. Cut out the states. Organize states according to common attributes as an extension of a social studies topic.

References

Bereska, C., L. C. Bolster, C. A. Bolster, and R. Scheaffer. 1998. *Exploring statistics in the elementary grades: Book one, grades k–6*. White Plains, NY: Dale Seymour.

Franklin, C., G. Kader, D. Mewborn, J. Moreno, R. Peck, M. Perry, and R. Scheaffer. 2007. *Guidelines for assessment and instruction in statistics education (GAISE) report: A pre-k–12 curriculum framework*. Alexandria, VA: American Statistical Association. *www.amstat.org/education/gaise*.

National Council of Teachers of Mathematics. 2000. *Principles and standards for school mathematics*. Reston, VA: National Council of Teachers of Mathematics.

Common Core State Standards for Mathematics. www.corestandards.org.

DESCRIBING DISTRIBUTIONS

INVESTIGATION 3.1
HOW MANY POCKETS?

Overview

This investigation focuses on students collecting, analyzing, and interpreting numerical data. After listening to the story *A Pocket for Corduroy*, by Don Freeman, students generate questions about how many pockets they have in their clothes. Students count the number of pockets in their clothing. Data by the class are collected on sticky notes and organized, displayed, and compared in a **dotplot**.

GAISE Components

This investigation follows the four components of statistical problem solving put forth in the *Guidelines for Assessment and Instruction in Statistics Education (GAISE) Report*. The four components are formulate a statistical question that can be answered with data, design and implement a plan to collect appropriate data, analyze the collected data by graphical and numerical methods, and interpret the results of the analysis in the context of the original question. This is a GAISE Level A activity.

Learning Goals

Students will be able to do the following after completing this investigation:

- Generate questions about the number of pockets in their clothing
- Organize and display data in a dotplot
- Analyze data and record observations
- Compare two groups of data using dotplots

Common Core State Standards for Mathematical Practice

1. Make sense of problems and persevere in solving them.
2. Reason abstractly and quantitatively.
3. Construct viable arguments and critique the reasoning of others.
4. Model with mathematics.

Common Core State Standards
Grade Level Content

K.CC.7 Compare two numbers between 1 and 10 presented as written numerals.

Note: The Common Core State Standards do not include the dotplot as a statistical graph until the sixth grade. However, the writers of this publication feel a dotplot is an excellent visual representation of organizing numbers between 1 and 10 and have included its use in this investigation at this beginning grade level.

NCTM Principles and Standards
for School Mathematics

Data Analysis and Probability

Pre-K–2 All students should pose questions and gather data about themselves and their surroundings; sort and classify objects according to their attributes and organize data about the objects; and represent data using concrete objects, pictures, and graphs.

Materials

- Grid chart paper
- Sticky notes (2 colors – green and yellow)

Estimated Time

One day

Instructional Plan

✏️ Formulate a Statistical Question

1. Read *A Pocket for Corduroy*, by Don Freeman.

> In this story, Lisa and her mother go to the Laundromat. Lisa brings her stuffed bear, Corduroy. Corduroy sees Lisa searching through her pockets before putting clothes in the washer. Corduroy notices he doesn't have a pocket and goes in search of one. He gets lost and spends the night in the Laundromat. The next day, Lisa returns, takes him home, and makes a pocket for him.

2. After reading the story, ask your students if they share Corduroy's desire for pockets in their clothes. Ask your students if they have pockets in the clothes they are wearing today. How many pockets do they have? Do boys and girls have the same number of pockets in their clothes? Discuss if you want your students to count their indoor clothes and outdoor clothes, or just their indoor clothes. Discuss what counts as a pocket.

The remainder of this investigation focuses on the question, "Do boys and girls have the same number of pockets in their clothes?"

Before collecting data, you may want to ask your students to raise their hands if they think girls have more pockets. Then, ask your students to raise their hands if they think boys have more pockets. Let students know they were making a prediction when they raised their hand and that they will use their number of pockets as data to see if their prediction about whether boys or girls have more pockets was correct.

✏ Collect Appropriate Data

1. Have each student count the number of pockets in their clothing and record the number on a sticky note. Boys should write their number on one color of sticky note and girls on a different color of sticky note.

2. Draw a number line on the grid paper. The scale should start at 0 and go to the largest number of pockets observed by your students. The numbers should be equally spaced on the horizontal axis. Label the horizontal axis *Number of Pockets*.

3. Have students place their sticky note (number of pockets) above the number on the number line. To begin with, put all notes—whether from boys or from girls—vertically above the appropriate number. Figure 3.1.1 shows an example of a dotplot of the number of pockets from a group of first-graders.

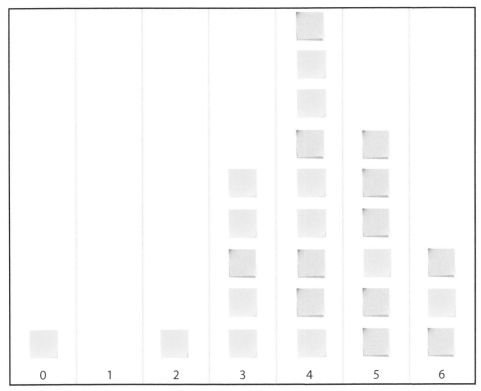

Number of Pockets

Figure 3.1.1 Dotplot of number of pockets

✎ Analyze the Data

1. Ask the following questions:

    a. What is the lowest number of pockets? This is called the minimum.

    b. What is the highest number of pockets? This is called the maximum.

    c. What is the number of pockets that occurs most often? This number is called the mode. (The mode is four pockets in this example. It occurs nine times.)

2. Ask your students if boys and girls have about the same number of pockets. Because the data are mixed, suggest they make two graphs—one for the boys and the other for the girls. For comparison purposes, the two scales should be the same.

3. Draw a number line on another sheet of grid chart paper. Place this sheet next to the graph already constructed. Take the boys' sticky notes from the first graph and transfer to the new graph. The girls' sticky notes may need to be adjusted on the first graph once the boys' sticky notes have been removed. Note that the use of grid chart paper helps keep the

rows lined up. Otherwise, it is easy to misrepresent comparing column heights. See Figures 3.1.2 and 3.1.3.

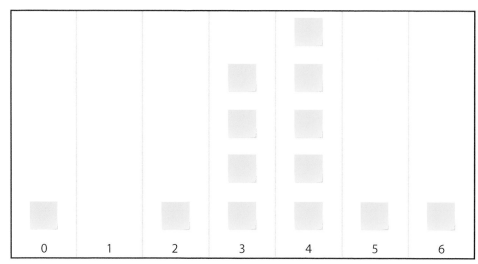

Number of Pockets

Figure 3.1.2 Dotplot of number of pockets for girls

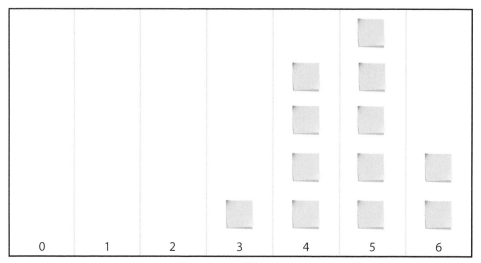

Number of Pockets

Figure 3.1.3 Dotplot of number of pockets for boys

4. Ask students the following questions:

   a. What is the minimum number of pockets for the girls? For the boys?

   b. What is the maximum number of pockets for the girls? For the boys?

   c. What is the mode number of pockets for the girls? For the boys?

d. How many boys have four or more pockets? What fraction of the boys have four or more pockets?

e. How many girls have four or more pockets? What fraction of the girls have four or more pockets?

✏️ **Interpret the Results in the Context of the Original Question**

1. Have your students recall that the original question was, "Do boys and girls have the same number of pockets in their clothes?" Have your students write a summary that begins with answering the question and then justifying their answer based on the analysis of the data conducted in class. They should include the data and graphs. They also should discuss how their prediction about whether boys or girls have more pockets compares to the actual data they collected.

2. Ask your students if they think their parents or grandparents have more or fewer pockets than they do? Why or why not?

3. Ask students how they might go about finding the answer to Question 2.

Example of 'Interpret the Results' 💿

Note: The following is not an example of actual student work, but an example of all the parts that should be included in student work.

After we listened to the story *A Pocket for Corduroy*, we became curious about the number of pockets we have on our clothes and whether girls or boys have more. So, on a green sticky note, each boy in our class wrote the number of pockets he had and the girls did the same thing, except their sticky notes were yellow. Then, we put them all in a dotplot. When we tried to answer our statistical question about whether girls or boys had more pockets, it was a little hard to do with all the green and yellow sticky notes together. So, to make it easier to answer our question, we drew two dotplots with the same scale, one for the boys and one for the girls.

By comparing the two dotplots, we concluded that, overall, boys have more pockets. We had to be careful because the number of boys and the number of girls was not the same. There were 12 boys and 13 girls. Still, 11 out of the 12 boys had four or more pockets; that's way over half of the boys. But 7 of the 13 girls, about half of them, had four or more pockets, so we concluded from our analysis that boys have more pockets than girls. We're going to continue this activity by asking our parents and grandparents how many pockets they usually have on their everyday clothes.

Assessment with Answers

A group of students counted the number of pockets in their clothes and drew the two graphs shown below.

Number of Pockets for Girls

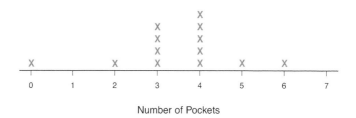

Figure 3.1.4 Dotplot of number of pockets for girls

Number of Pockets for Boys

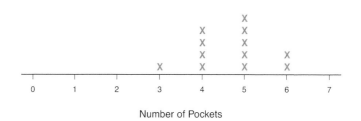

Figure 3.1.5 Dotplot of number of pockets for boys

1. What is the minimum number of pockets for the girls? The minimum number of pockets for the girls is zero.

2. What is the maximum number of pockets for the boys? The maximum number of pockets for the boys is six.

3. What is the mode number of pockets for the girls? The mode number of pockets for the girls is four.

4. How many more girls had four pockets than boys who had four pockets? There were five girls with four pockets each and four boys with four pockets each, so there was one more girl who had four pockets.

5. Who has more pockets, boys or girls? Use words, numbers, and graphs to explain your answer. Boys have more pockets than do girls. There are seven girls who have four, five, or six pockets, but there are 11 boys who have four, five, or six pockets. Every boy has three or more pockets, but there are two girls who have fewer than three pockets.

Extensions

1. Have your students collect data on the number of eyelets on their shoes. Students can compare the number of eyelets with the type of shoes. For example, compare the number of eyelets in gym shoes versus dress shoes.

2. Have your students ask their parents or an adult how many pockets they have. Have the students make a bar graph of the number of pockets from the adults and then compare those results with the class results.

3. Science connection: Have your students investigate what animals have pockets or pouches.

References

Chapin, S., A. Koziol, J. MacPherson, and C. Rezba. 2003. *Navigating through data analysis and probability in grades 3-5*. Reston, VA: National Council of Teachers of Mathematics.

Franklin, C., G. Kader, D. Mewborn, J. Moreno, R. Peck, M. Perry, and R. Scheaffer. 2007. *Guidelines for assessment and instruction in statistics education (GAISE) report: A pre-k–12 curriculum framework*. Alexandria, VA: American Statistical Association. *www.amstat.org/education/gaise*.

Freeman, D. 1978. *A pocket for corduroy.* New York, NY: Penguin Group Publishers.

Greenes, C. E. (ed.) 2002. *Navigating through data analysis and probability in prekindergarten – grade 2*. Reston, VA: National Council of Teachers of Mathematics.

National Council of Teachers of Mathematics. 2000. *Principles and standards for school mathematics*. Reston, VA: National Council of Teachers of Mathematics.

Common Core State Standards for Mathematics. www.corestandards.org.

Investigation 3.2
Who Has the Longest First Name?

Overview

This investigation is based on one found in the Appendix for Level A in *Guidelines for Assessment and Instruction in Statistics Education (GAISE): A Pre-K–12 Curriculum Framework*. During the first week of school, a third-grade teacher is trying to help her students learn one another's names by playing various games. During one of the games, a student named MacKenzie noticed that she and her classmate Zacharius each have nine letters in their names. MacKenzie conjectured that their names were longer than everyone else's names, which gave the teacher an opportunity to introduce a statistics lesson.

In this investigation, students analyze the length (number of letters) of their first names. The data will be organized and displayed in **dotplots** to develop the **median** as a measure of center and the **range** as a measure of variability of first name lengths.

GAISE Components

This investigation follows the four components of statistical problem solving put forth in the *Guidelines for Assessment and Instruction in Statistics Education (GAISE) Report*. The four components are formulate a statistical question that can be answered with data, design and implement a plan to collect appropriate data, analyze the collected data by graphical and numerical methods, and interpret the results of the analysis in the context of the original question. This is a GAISE Level A activity.

Learning Goals

Students will be able to do the following after completing this investigation:

- Collect data and organize the results in a dotplot

- Find measures of center (median and mode) for the data

- Consider what measures of center are appropriate for categorical versus quantitative data (addressed in the extensions)

- Find a measure of spread (range) for the data

Common Core State Standards
for Mathematical Practice

1. Make sense of problems and persevere in solving them.
2. Reason abstractly and quantitatively.
3. Construct viable arguments and critique the reasoning of others.
4. Model with mathematics.

Common Core State Standards
Grade Level Content

6.SP.1 Recognize a statistical question as one that anticipates variability in the data related to the question and accounts for it in the answers.

6.SP.2 Understand that a set of data collected to answer a statistical question has a distribution that can be described by its center, spread, and overall shape.

6.SP.3 Recognize that a measure of center for a numerical data set summarizes all its values with a single number, while a measure of variation describes how its values vary with a single number.

6.SP.4 Display numerical data in plots on a number line, including dotplots, histograms, and box plots.

NCTM Principles and Standards
for School Mathematics

Data Analysis and Probability

Grades 3-5 All students should design investigations to address a question and consider how data collection methods affect the nature of the data set; represent data using tables and graphs such as line plots, bar graphs, and line graphs; use measure of center, focusing on the median, and understand what each does and does not indicate about the data set.

Materials

- Sticky notes
- Masking tape

Estimated Time

Two days

Instructional Plan

✏ Formulate a Statistical Question

1. Have your students discuss what they would like to know about their first names. Make a list of their responses. The following are some possible responses:

   Do any of us have the same name?

   What is our most common first name?

   Who has the longest name?

   Who has the shortest name?

   What is the most common first letter?

   What is the most common length for our first names?

2. This investigation focuses on the statistical question, "How do the lengths of first names vary in our class?"

✏ Collect Appropriate Data

1. Hand out a sticky note to each student. Have your students write their first name on a sticky note, as well as the number of letters in their first name. For example:

2. Have your students place their sticky notes on the board in no particular order. They are placed randomly so that the class will be able to observe

how a dotplot can be used to organize the notes. Figure 3.2.1 is an example of the data for one class.

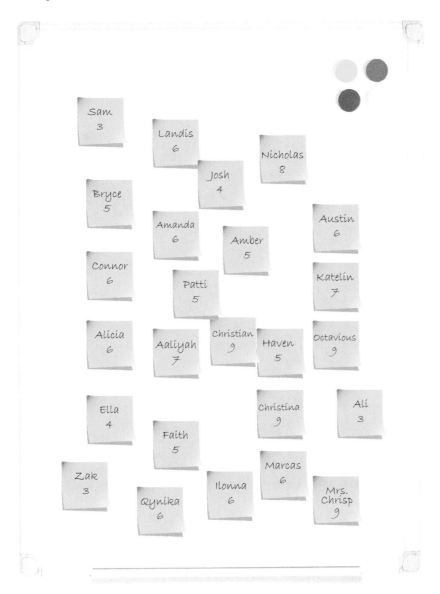

Figure 3.2.1 Example of sticky notes with names and lengths

✏ **Analyze the Data**

Have your students discuss how they may be able to organize all these sticky notes. They may suggest grouping the notes by the number of letters, as shown in Figure 3.2.2.

Figure 3.2.2 Example of sticky notes organized by number of letters

Reorganize the sticky notes into a preliminary dotplot. Note that, as much as possible, there should be no gaps or overlaps between each note in a column. See Figure 3.2.3.

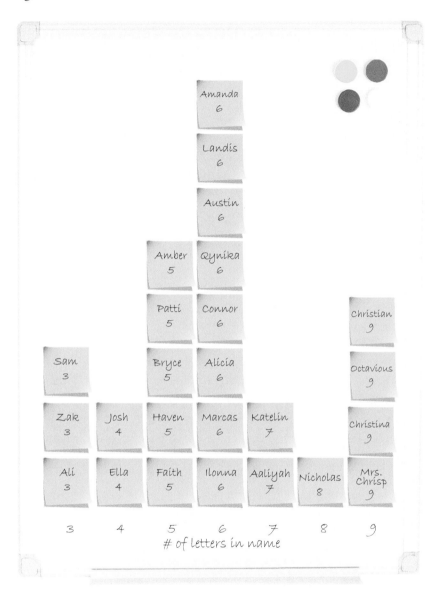

Figure 3.2.3 Dotplot of length of first names

Ask the following questions:

a. What is the shortest name? How many letters does it have?

b. What is the longest name? How many letters does it have?

c. Is it possible for someone to have a name shorter than our shortest name?

d. Is it possible for someone to have a name longer than our longest name?

e. What is the range of the data? The range of the data is the largest number minus the smallest number. (9 – 3 = 6 for this example)

f. What is the most common number of letters in the first names for our class? This value is called the mode. (6 for this example)

To introduce the concept of the median, students need to be lined up side by side according to the number of letters in their name. Note that it might be helpful to have your students form a human dotplot first. That will get all the students together who have the same number of letters.

a. Put a piece of masking tape on the floor labeled with numbers from the smallest number of letters to the largest number of letters in their names.

Figure 3.2.4 Labeled masking tape

b. Have your students line up corresponding to the length of their name (e.g., Josh and Ella would both line up above the 4) in either order. Once they have created a human dotplot, have them form a single-file line side-by-side, keeping them in order based on the length of their name.

c. Ask your students who they think is exactly in the middle of this display.

d. Have one student each at either end of the line sit down until one student is left standing in the middle. If there is an even number of students in the class, you may want to include yourself in the display to ensure students will be finding the median of an odd number of data points. For example, have the first student above 3 (Zak) and the last student above 9 (Octavious) sit down at the same time. Have the second student above 3 (Sam) and the second-to-last student above 9 (Christian) sit down at the same time. Continue this process until you are left with one person standing. The number of letters in that person's name is the median of the data set. Note that if the number of students is even, there will be two students left standing. The median is the value half-way between their values.

e. Ask your students how they could use the dotplot on the board with the sticky notes to model what they did in the human dotplot in order to find the median length of their names. Have your students make suggestions. They should realize that they could either remove sticky notes one at a time from both ends until one was left or put an X through the notes until they get to the middle one, in the case of an odd number of sticky notes.

f. A new student arrives after the above has been completed. Her name is Seraphinia. How would adding her to the data set affect the center measures of mode and median and the spread measure of range? Note that Seraphinia has 10 letters, so the mode remains at 6. Also note that, with Seraphinia, there is now an even number of names. An even number of data points creates two "middles." The median is taken to be the value half-way between the two middles. In this example, both middle values are 6, so the median remains at 6. The range is now 10 − 3 = 7, an increase of one letter.

✏ Interpret the Results in the Context of the Original Question

1. Have your students recall the original question: How do the lengths of first names vary in our class? Ask them to write a report that answers the question, along with providing a justification of it using their analysis.

2. Ask your students the following questions:

   a. Based on our data, what is the most common or typical length of our first names?

   b. Do you think this would be the same in the classroom across the hall? Why or why not?

   c. Do you think this would be the same in a middle- or high-school classroom? Why or why not?

   d. Do you think this would be the same in Mexico? In China?

Example of 'Interpret the Results'

Note: The following is not an example of actual student work, but an example of all the parts that should be included in student work.

On the first day of school, our teacher had us play games to learn each other's names. After that, she was showing us some statistics by having us study the lengths of our first names. The question was, "How do the lengths of first names vary in our class?"

We used sticky notes with our names and the number of letters in our names written on them. After putting all of the sticky notes on the board all messed up, we organized them into a dotplot with the number of letters on the horizontal axis. But, we didn't do the graph the right way the first time, because we didn't keep the columns nice and straight and in line with the other columns. We had to remember to keep the rows in line, also. When we corrected that, we saw that there were more of us whose first names had six letters than any other number. It was the highest in the dotplot. That's called the mode number of letters.

We also calculated the middle number of letters by lining up from fewest number of letters to most and then having low and high sit down until we got to one person left. That number is called the median. It's the middle number of letters, 6 (Alicia), with 12 of us below Alicia and 12 of us above Alicia.

The day after we did that analysis, we got a new student in class, Seraphinia. When we added her, she had the longest name. The range of letters was 9 − 3 = 6 before Seraphinia, but 10 − 3 = 7 letters with her. The mode stayed at 6 because it was still the highest. To find the median, we sat down like before, but now there were two middles, Alicia and Connor. They both have 6 letters in their names, so the median is still 6.

We want to continue doing this study by looking at names from different countries to see if their number of letters differs from ours. We think that maybe Chinese names are shorter.

Assessment with Answers

With the help of his family and friends, Jose collected data regarding the lengths of first names of his family and friends. Table 3.2.1 shows the data Jose collected.

Table 3.2.1 Length of First Name

	Family and Friends First Names	Number of Letters in First Name
1	Hector	6
2	Amada	5
3	Che	3
4	Ricardo	6
5	Camila	6
6	Roberto	7
7	Carlos	6
8	Raymundo	8
9	Gabriela	8
10	Diego	5
11	Tia	3

1. Make a dotplot of the length of the first names of Jose's family and friends.

2. Find the value of each of the following:

   Maximum value: 8

   Minimum value: 3

   Mode: 6

   Median: 6

   Range: 5

3. Write a summary of what you observed about the length of the first names of Jose's family and friends. Your summary should include reference to the dotplot and the measures of center and spread that you found. The dotplot shows that all of the name lengths are from 3–8 letters long. The most common length was 6 letters (four people had this length) and the median length was also 6 letters, meaning there were five names above the median (6, 6, 7, 8, 8) and five below (3, 3, 5, 5, 6).

Extensions

1. Have your students do an analysis of the length of their last names.

2. Your students may have had the experience of having to write their full name (first, last, and space between) on a form that has a set of boxes. Have your students combine the length of their first and last names, including the space between their names, and investigate how many boxes the form should have so most of the students in class can fill in their entire name.

   Note: Discuss with your students what they feel "most of the students" means in this context. Some students will think just over half, while others will want to say all except for one or two students. Some may even interpret it as "most often" and want to use the mode. Allow students to answer the question based on their definition of "most."

3. Students may be tempted to find the median of a categorical set of data. The following exercise will demonstrate why the median is a measure of center for numerical data only.

   a. Consider the statistical question, "What is your favorite type of pet?" Put a piece of masking tape on the floor labeled as follows:

   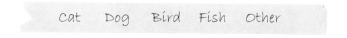

   Figure 3.2.5 Favorite pet

   Have your students line up according to their favorite type of pet, thus forming a human bar graph. They have to choose only one pet category.

b. Ask your students which type of pet is the most popular? Who thinks their favorite type of pet is in the middle?

Note: The first question is asking for the mode, while the second question is designed to begin a discussion about why categorical data do not have a median. The following parts, c through e, should help with the discussion.

c. Recalling the process of creating a human dotplot to determine the median length of first names, have your students at either end sit down until one is left standing in the middle (two if the number of students is even). Ask your students what the median is. Students might respond with the name of the student or the type of pet.

d. Change the order in which the pets are listed on the floor and have your students make a new bar graph.

Figure 3.2.6 Favorite pet

e. Have your students find the middle again by sitting down starting at each end. Ask what the median or middle is. It is likely that this answer will be different from the first bar graph. Discuss with your students that changing the order of the categories has changed the median response, but the data are exactly the same in both cases. Have them do the process a third time. Yet another median appears for the same data. Discuss with your students that a median cannot have different values for the same data set. So, finding a median for categorical data does not make sense. To find a median, data must be able to be ordered from smallest to largest. That can be done for numerical data, but it cannot be done for categorical data.

4. Ask the class to work together to determine if the following data sets can have a median: number of pets, eye color, number of siblings, ways to get to school. Then, have your students work in pairs to create an example of a data set that could have a median and one that could not have a median. They should write a sentence or two with their examples, explaining why their data set can or cannot have a median.

References

Bereska, C., L. C. Bolster, C. A. Bolster, and R. Scheaffer. 1998. *Exploring statistics in the elementary grades: Book one, grades k–6*. White Plains, NY: Dale Seymour.

Franklin, C., G. Kader, D. Mewborn, J. Moreno, R. Peck, M. Perry, and R. Scheaffer. 2007. *Guidelines for assessment and instruction in statistics education (GAISE) report: A pre-k–12 curriculum framework*. Alexandria, VA: American Statistical Association. *www.amstat.org/education/gaise*.

National Council of Teachers of Mathematics. 2000. *Principles and standards for school mathematics*. Reston, VA: National Council of Teachers of Mathematics.

Common Core State Standards for Mathematics. www.corestandards.org.

INVESTIGATION 3.3
HOW EXPENSIVE IS YOUR NAME?

Overview

This investigation focuses on developing the **mean** as a measure of center. In addition, students will compare two sets of numerical data and build on the objectives in Investigation 3.2, "Who Has the Longest First Name?" Students will collect data regarding the amount of money it would cost to monogram their first name on a shirt. The mean, median, and mode will be compared for the number of letters in their first name and for the total worth of their first name. Students will be asked to focus on the shapes of the distributions and the idea that although the scale of the distributions shifted, the shape of the distributions remained the same.

GAISE Components

This investigation follows the four components of statistical problem solving put forth in the *Guidelines for Assessment and Instruction in Statistics Education (GAISE) Report.* The four components are formulate a statistical question that can be answered with data, design and implement a plan to collect appropriate data, analyze the collected data by graphical and numerical methods, and interpret the results of the analysis in the context of the original question. This is a GAISE Level B activity.

Learning Goals

Students will be able to do the following after completing this investigation:

- Collect data and organize the results in a dotplot

- Find measures of center (mean, median, and mode) for the data

- Compare two distributions by using measures of center and the shapes of the distributions

Common Core State Standards
for Mathematical Practice

1. Make sense of problems and persevere in solving them.
2. Reason abstractly and quantitatively.
3. Construct viable arguments and critique the reasoning of others.
4. Model with mathematics.

Common Core State Standards
Grade Level Content

6.EE.2 Write, read, and evaluate expressions in which letters stand for numbers.

6.SP.1 Recognize a statistical question as one that anticipates variability in the data related to the question and accounts for it in the answers.

6.SP.2 Understand that a set of data collected to answer a statistical question has a distribution that can be described by its center, spread, and overall shape.

6.SP.3 Recognize that a measure of center for a numerical data set summarizes all its values with a single number, while a measure of variation describes how its values vary with a single number.

6.SP.4 Display numerical data in plots on a number line, including dotplots, histograms, and boxplots.

NCTM Principles and Standards
for School Mathematics

Data Analysis and Probability

Grades 3-5 All students should describe the shape and important features of a set of data and compare related data sets, with an emphasis on how the data are distributed.

Grades 6-8 All students should formulate questions, design studies, and collect data about a characteristic shared by two populations or different characteristics within one population; find, use, and interpret measures of center and spread, including mean and interquartile range.

Materials

- Sticky notes
- Interlocking cubes (e.g., Unifix cubes)
- Chart paper

Estimated Time

Two days

Instructional Plan

✏️ Formulate a Question

1. Before beginning this investigation, display on the board the dotplot of the number of letters in your students' first names. This plot was made in Investigation 3.2, "Who Has the Longest First Name?" If you do not have this graph, you should collect the length of each student's first name and make a dotplot of the data. See Figure 3.3.1.

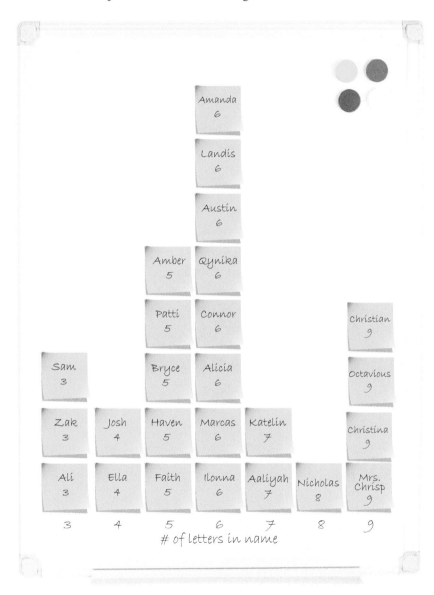

Figure 3.3.1 Dotplot of length of first names 💿

2. Begin this investigation by asking your students where they have seen a person's name printed on a shirt or jersey. Share with your students that some people have their initials monogrammed or sewn on their dress shirts or a piece of luggage. Explain to your students that, in many of those cases, there is a charge to sew the letters on the shirt. Suggest to your students that you wonder how much it would cost to have their names sewn onto a school T-shirt. Tell your students to assume it costs 5¢ per letter to sew their name on a T-shirt.

3. Explain to your students that the statistical question they will be focusing on is "How expensive is it to monogram first names onto T-shirts?" and how this question is related to the question from Investigation 3.2, "How do the lengths of first names vary in our class?"

4. Refer to the dotplot (Figure 3.3.1) of the length of your students' first names and explain to your students that they are going to make a dotplot of the cost of sewing their first name on a T-shirt. Ask your students how this new plot will be similar and different from the plot on the board.

✏️ Collect Appropriate Data

1. Have your students write their names on a sticky note, along with the cost for sewing on their first name. (See Figure 3.3.2.)

2. Have your students put their sticky notes on the board. Do not attempt to organize the sticky notes at this time.

Figure 3.3.2 Sticky note of first name and cost of sewing on first name

✏️ Analyze the Data

1. Have your students discuss how the sticky notes could be organized. Encourage them to group the notes by cost.

2. Arrange the sticky notes to create a dotplot. Place this plot alongside the "length of name" plot. Figure 3.3.3 is an example of a dotplot

based on the names shown in Investigation 3.2, "Who Has the Longest First Name?"

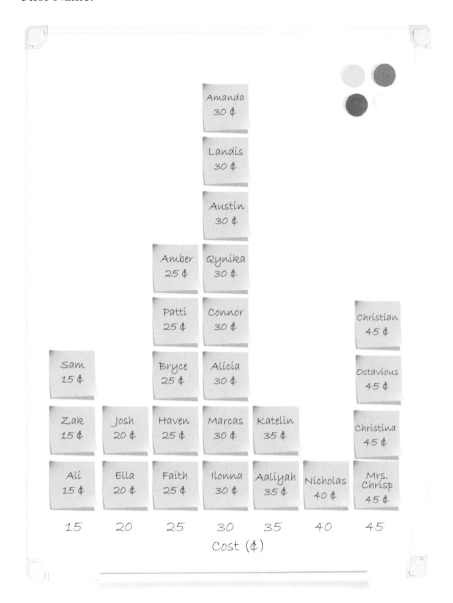

Figure 3.3.3 Dot plot of the cost of sewing on letters

3. Refer to the dotplot of the cost of sewing on the names and ask the following questions:

   a. Who has the least expensive name to sew on? How much does this name cost to sew on? Are these the same students who had the shortest names?

b. What is the most expensive name to sew on? How much does this name cost to sew on? Are these the same students who had the longest names?

c. What is the most common cost to sew on a name (i.e., the **mode**)? Note that the mode is 30 cents. Some students will incorrectly want to answer 8, the frequency of the mode.

d. How does the mode for the cost of sewing on the letters compare to the mode for the number of letters in your first names? Note that the mode of the cost of sewing on the letters data is five times the mode of the length of name data.

4. What is the **median**, or middle number, for the length of name plot? **Note:** If you have not discussed how to find the median of a set of data, see Investigation 3.2, "Who Has the Longest First Name?"

5. What is the median (middle) cost for sewing names?

6. Ask your students how the median cost for sewing on a name compares to the median number of letters in first names. **Note:** The median of the sewing cost data will be five times the median of the length of name data.

7. Introduce the concept of **mean** by developing the "fair share" sense of measuring the center of the data set of number of letters in first names.

a. The data set in this example has 25 students. Divide these students into five groups of four students, with the sixth group having five students.

b. Instruct your students that they will need as many interlocking cubes as there are letters in their names. For example, Josh will need four interlocking cubes because his name has four letters.

c. You want your students to discover that another measure of center for a set of data (in addition to the mode and median) is based on distributing the data evenly among the subjects, a "fair share" concept. In mathematics, the operation of division creates a fair share distribution of n data points among k subjects. For example, if four students have a total of 28 letters in their names, then each of them would have a fair share number of 28/4 = 7 letters. In statistics, this number is called the average, or **mean**, number of letters (i.e., the number of letters each student would have were each to have the same number of letters). To this end, here is a suggestion to follow:

i. Have the groups discuss what the mode and median centers are for their names. Note that if there are no duplications, then there is no mode. Ask them to describe how the mode measures the center of a data set (most often). Ask them to describe how the median measures the center of a data set (middle of the ordered values). Ask them to determine another description of center; lead them to a fair share, even distribution, leveling off concept (mean).

ii. Have them demonstrate the fair share concept with their cubes in two ways. Suppose that one group of four students has a total of 28 letters in their first names (e.g., Sara, Landis, Octavious, Christian).

1. For this group, combine all 28 cubes and then distribute them one by one until they are all distributed. Each of the four students will have 7 cubes, the mean for that group.

2. An alternative procedure is to instruct each student to have a stack of cubes equal to the number of letters in his/her name. Then, move cubes from one stack to another, trying to equalize their stacks so all the stacks have the same number of cubes. Each will have 7 cubes, the mean. Note that Sara and Landis will gain cubes, while Octavious and Christian need to share some of theirs.

iii. In most cases, there will be cubes left over. Have your students discuss what to do with the leftovers so that they can be distributed evenly. For example, suppose a group of four students were Ali, Amanda, Marcas, and Aaliyah. They have a total of 22 letters. So, when distributed evenly, each will have five cubes with two left over. The two need to be split in half, with each student getting one of the halves. So, the mean would be five and a half. Another way to handle the leftovers is to see how far the two leftovers can be distributed around the group of four students. Clearly, the two would cover half of the four students (i.e., halfway around).

Note: Each group of students now knows how to find the mean for their set of four or five students. Ask them how they would find the mean number of letters in the first names for all the students in the class. Some may suggest that what they did in their individual group would have to be extended and done using the whole class. (There is a total of 148 letters, which, when divided by 25, yields a mean of 5 and 23/25 letters.)

> **Mode, Median, and Mean Are Centers**
>
> The **mode** is whatever there is the most of. The **median** is the middle value of ordered numerical data, and the **mean** is the "fair share" value.

Others might suggest the mean of the class would be the fair share mean of the group means. This would be correct if all the groups were the same size. See the extension at the end of this investigation to determine what to do when not all of the groups are the same size.

8. Have your class determine the class mean number of letters in their first names and then ask them what the mean cost of sewing on the names for the entire class is. They should answer that the mean cost is five times the mean number of letters. They also could find the mean cost of sewing the names for the class by using the information in the dotplot, adding the cost of all the names and dividing by the number of students in the class (i.e., fair share).

Shape of a Distribution

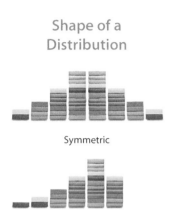

Symmetric

Skewed

9. Examine the **shape of a distribution**.

   a. Ask your students to look at the distribution (dotplot) of the lengths of names and the distribution (dotplot) of the costs of sewing on the names.

   b. Ask your students not to focus on the numbers in the display, but rather on the way the distribution is shaped. (Trace the top of the distributions with your finger as you are showing them what to focus on.)

   c. Ask your students how the shape of the distribution for the cost of sewing on the names compares to the shape of the distribution for the number of letters in their first names. They should realize that the shapes are similar, even though the cost dotplot was shifted to the right. Ask them to discuss why the dotplots should have a similar shape. They should realize that since each letter cost 5 cents, the distribution shifted by a factor of 5. This occurred because the original data were used to determine how much a letter would cost to sew on. As a result, each data point was multiplied by 5 to determine the cost of sewing on the name. Note that this also explains why the mode, median, and mean changed by a factor of 5 cents.

   Note: The students also should notice that if the dotplots are drawn on the same scale, the cost dotplot has more variability than does the names dotplot. Measures of variability are discussed in Investigation 3.4, "How Long Are Our Shoes?"

   ✏ Interpret the Results in the Context of the Original Question

   Recall the original question, "How expensive is it to sew first names onto a T-shirt?" Also recall that it was coupled with "How do the lengths of first names vary in our class?" The investigation focused on comparing the centers and shapes of the two distributions. Ask your students to write a report that discusses how the two distributions were similar and how and why they differed. They are to provide an answer by including graphs and measures they formulated in their analysis.

Example of 'Interpret the Results'

Note: The following is not an example of actual student work, but an example of all the parts that should be included in student work.

In a previous activity, we analyzed the number of letters in first names by drawing a dotplot that looked like this for our class.

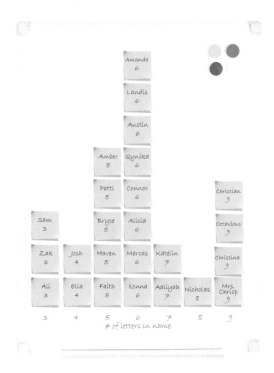

Our student council voted to have T-shirts made with our first names on them and asked our class to do a statistical study on the cost. So, we made a statistical question of "How expensive is it to sew first names onto T-shirts?" We asked our domestic arts teacher what it would cost to do the sewing. She said most embroidery businesses would charge around 5 cents per letter. With that estimate, we first determined the data set for the cost of sewing first names based on our data set for the number of letters in our first names. For example, Janice has six letters in her name, so her cost would be five times six, or 30 cents. We did that for all 25 students in our class and produced the following dotplot:

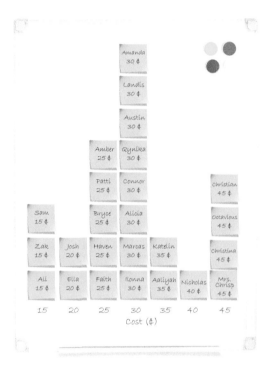

We decided to compare our two dotplots. The first thing is that the scales are different. The number of letters scale is 3, 4, 5, 6, 7, 8, 9. The cost of sewing scale is 15, 20, 25, 30, 35, 40, 45. It is five times the letters scale. This makes sense since each letter costs 5 cents.

From our last study, we found the mode (most often) number of letters was 6 and the median (middle) number of letters was also 6. So it makes sense that the mode and median for the cost data set should be five times as much (i.e., 30 cents). Our teacher had us learn another measure of center called the mean. It is a fair share, or equal number, for everyone.

What we did was work in groups of four, and working with cubes that represented the number of letters in our names, put them all together in a pile and then handed them out to each other. If we had done that for our whole class according to our dotplot, all the letters in our first names would have totaled 148. Handing them out to all 25 of us gave each of us 5 cubes with 23 cubes left over. To hand out the 23 evenly, each of us would get 23/25 of a cube, so the mean (fair share) center is 5 23/25 letters for the whole data set.

After we found that the mean number of letters was 5 23/25, we found the mean cost of the letters by multiplying 5 23/25 by 5 (the cost of each letter).

The answer was a mean cost of 29 3/5 cents, which was the cost each one of us would have if we all had the same cost.

The last thing we did was to compare the shapes of the two dotplots. We saw that they were the same except the cost one was more spread out. Just like we find measures of center (mode, median, mean), our teacher said we also will learn how to measure how spread out a data set is. We can't wait to find out.

Assessment with Answers

1. Jose collected first names from his family and friends. Table 3.3.1 shows the first names and their lengths. Determine the amount of money it would cost for each family member to have their first name sewn on a T-shirt with a cost of 4 cents per letter and complete the last column in Table 3.3.1.

Table 3.3.1 Cost to Sew on First Name

	Family and Friends First Name	Number of Letters in First Name	Cost to Sew on First Name
1	Hector	6	24 ¢
2	Amada	5	20 ¢
3	Che	3	12 ¢
4	Ricardo	6	24 ¢
5	Camila	6	24 ¢
6	Roberto	7	28 ¢
7	Carlos	6	24 ¢
8	Raymundo	8	32 ¢
9	Gabriela	8	32 ¢
10	Diego	5	20 ¢
11	Tia	3	12 ¢

2. Find the mean, median, and mode of the number of letters.

	Number of Letters	Cost of Letters
Mean	5.73	22.92 ¢
Median	6	24 ¢
Mode	6	24 ¢

3. Use words, numbers, and graphs to explain how the mean, median, and mode of the number of letters compare to the mean, median, and mode of the cost of the letters. A dotplot of each data set should be included with the location of the mean, median, and mode labeled on the graph. The mean, median, and mode for the cost of the letters are four times the number of letters.

Length of First Names

Number of Letters

Cost to Sew on Letters

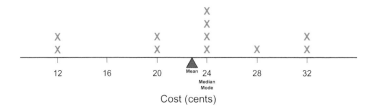

Cost (cents)

Extension

Introduce the concept of a weighted mean.

1. Place students in different sized groups of 3, 4, and 5.

2. Have each group find the mean length of their first names. Record the size of each group and the group mean.

3. Ask your students whether the mean of the entire class can be found by adding the group means and dividing by the number of groups. Discuss with them that this cannot be done because not all the groups are the same size. Ask them to verify that it could be done if the groups sizes were the same.

4. Discuss with your students the following method for using group means based on different group sizes to find the class mean.

    a. To find the class mean, all lengths have to be collected and distributed equally to the class members. To find the total value of the lengths, multiply the group means by the number of members in the group and add the results. The sum is the total length of first names. Finally, divide the total length by the number of students in the class.

An example:
Assume there were three groups. Group 1 had four students with a mean of 4.25 letters. Group 2 had four students with a mean of 4.5 letters. Group 3 had three students with a mean of 5 letters. To find the mean number of letters for the class, calculate the following:

$$\frac{(4 \times 4.25) + (4 \times 4.5) + (3 \times 5)}{11} = \frac{17 + 18 + 15}{11} = \frac{50}{11} = 4\frac{6}{11}$$

    a. Ask your students what 4 x 4.25, 4 x 4.5, and 3 x 5 represent.

    b. Ask your students what the 50 in the calculation represents.

    c. Ask your students what the unit is for 4 6/11.

    d. Ask your students to explain what 4 6/11 means in words. Note that they could say that each would have 4 5/11 letters if all 11 students had first names that were the same length.

References

Franklin, C., G. Kader, D. Mewborn, J. Moreno, R. Peck, M. Perry, and R. Scheaffer. 2007. *Guidelines for assessment and instruction in statistics education (GAISE) report: A pre-k–12 curriculum framework*. Alexandria, VA: American Statistical Association. *www.amstat.org/education/gaise*.

National Council of Teachers of Mathematics. 2000. *Principles and standards for school mathematics*. Reston, VA: National Council of Teachers of Mathematics.

Common Core State Standards for Mathematics. www.corestandards.org.

INVESTIGATION 3.4
HOW LONG ARE OUR SHOES?

Overview

In Investigation 1.1, "What Color Are Our Shoes," the focus was on students collecting, analyzing, and interpreting **categorical** data related to the color of their shoes. This investigation does the same for **numerical** data related to students' shoes. Students generate questions about what they would like to know about their shoes (e.g., length, number of eyelets). Decisions about how to conduct appropriate measurements and units are made. Graphs such as dotplots and boxplots are drawn to illustrate the data. Measures of center (**mode, median, mean**) and spread (**range, IQR, mean absolute deviation**) are computed. The detection of **outliers**, unusual values, will be explored. Conclusions are drawn based on the analysis in the context of the question(s) asked. This activity is based on an activity in *Exploring Statistics in the Elementary Grades: Book One, Grades K–6*, by Carolyn Bereska, L. Carey Bolster, Cyrilla A. Bolster, and Richard Scheaffer.

Note: If measuring the length of shoes or feet is not appropriate for your students, you may substitute hand span and call the investigation "How Wide Are Our Hands?"

GAISE Components

This investigation follows the four components of statistical problem solving put forth in the *Guidelines for Assessment and Instruction in Statistics Education (GAISE) Report*. The four components are formulate a statistical question that can be answered with data, design and implement a plan to collect appropriate data, analyze the collected data by graphical and numerical methods, and interpret the results of the analysis in the context of the original question. This is a GAISE Level B activity.

Learning Goals

Students will be able to do the following after completing this investigation:

- Make measurements in centimeters

- Calculate measures of center (mode, median, mean) and spread (range, interquartile range, mean absolute deviation) for a data set

- Display data in a dotplot and boxplot and observe clusters, gaps, and outliers

Common Core State Standards
for Mathematical Practices

1. Make sense of problems and persevere in solving them.

2. Reason abstractly and quantitatively.

3. Construct viable arguments and critique the reasoning of others.

4. Model with mathematics.

6. Attend to precision.

Common Core State Standards
Grade Level Content

6.SP.1 Recognize a statistical question as one that anticipates variability in the data related to the question and accounts for it in the answers.

6.SP.2 Understand that a set of data collected to answer a statistical question has a distribution that can be described by its center, spread, and overall shape.

6.SP.3 Recognize that a measure of center for a numerical data set summarizes all of its values with a single number, while a measure of variation describes how its values vary with a single number.

6.SP.4 Display numerical data in plots on a number line, including dotplots, histograms, and boxplots.

6.SP.5 Summarize numerical data sets in relation to their context, such as by:

a. Reporting the number of observations

b. Describing the nature of the attribute under investigation, including how it was measured and its units of measurement

c. Giving quantitative measures of center (median and/or mean) and variability (interquartile range and/or mean absolute deviation), as well as describing any overall pattern and any striking deviations from the overall pattern with reference to the context in which the data were gathered

d. Relating the choice of measures of center and variability to the shape of the data distribution and the context in which the data were gathered

NCTM Principles and Standards for School Mathematics

Data Analysis and Probability

Grades 6–8 All students should formulate questions that can be addressed with data and collect, organize, and display relevant data to answer them; select and use appropriate statistical methods to analyze data; find, use, and interpret measures of center and spread, including mean and interquartile range; discuss and understand the correspondence between data sets and their graphical representations, especially histograms, stemplots, boxplots, and scatterplots.

Materials

- Centimeter rulers

Estimated Time

2–3 days

Instructional Plan

✏️ Formulate a Statistical Question

Begin this investigation by holding up one of your student's shoes. Ask your students to write questions they would be interested in investigating about middle-school students' shoes. Possible questions might be the following:

    a. How many eyelets are in shoes?

    b. How long are shoelaces?

    c. How long is a middle-school student's shoe?

    d. Is the ratio of the length of a shoe to the width of a shoe a constant?

This investigation is based on the question, "How long is a middle-school student's shoe?"

✏️ Collect Appropriate Data

Before students begin measuring, discuss questions that need to be answered, including the following:

    1. Should feet or shoes be measured?

    2. Should the right or left shoe/foot be measured? One's right and left feet are not necessarily the same length.

3. If a shoe is chosen, should it be measured on or off the foot?

4. What unit of measurement should be used, inches or centimeters?

5. How can we be sure the measure is taken accurately? All measurements need to be taken in the same manner.

This investigation is based on measuring the shoe, in centimeters, that corresponds to the dominant foot (identified as the one mostly used when kicking something like a football). The shoe is kept on the foot, and the measurement is taken to the nearest whole number.

To minimize measurement error, tape a centimeter ruler to the floor with 0 at the wall. Students work in pairs. One student will press his or her heel against the wall as he/she steps on the ruler. The other will measure the length of the shoe by pressing another ruler vertically against the toe of the shoe, marking the distance the shoe is from the wall. The students will then switch roles. Table 3.4.1 shows a sample set of shoe length data collected from a class of sixth-graders.

Table 3.4.1 Sample Set of Shoe Length Data (cm)

| 20 | 17 | 17 | 19 | 20 | 17 | 19 | 14 | 17 | 20 | 15 | 19 | |
| 18 | 15 | 21 | 17 | 14 | 16 | 23 | 16 | 18 | 19 | 16 | 18 | 18 |

✏ Analyze the Data

1. In the analysis of the data, the students should focus on the shape, center, and spread. The first step is to look at the shape of the distribution. Begin by organizing the data in a frequency table. Table 3.4.2 shows the frequency table for the sample sixth-grade class.

Table 3.4.2 Frequency Table of Sample Sixth-Grade Class Data

Length	14	15	16	17	18	19	20	21	22	23
Tally	||	||	|||	⋏||	||||	||||	|||					
Frequency	2	2	3	5	4	4	3	1	0	1

Note: Even though no student's shoe length is 22 cm, it must be listed in the frequency table so the list of lengths is consecutive.

2. To further analyze shape, have the students make a dotplot.

   a. After making a dotplot of the class data, discuss with the students

the shape of the distribution with any evidence of clusters, gaps, and outliers. Figure 3.4.1 is a dotplot of the sample sixth-grade class data.

Length of Shoes

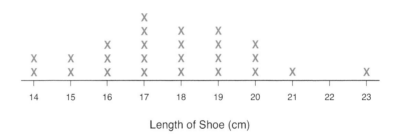

Length of Shoe (cm)

Figure 3.4.1 Dotplot of sample sixth-grade class data

Note: In this example, the shape of the distribution is fairly symmetrical and somewhat mound-shaped with a short gap between 21 and 23 cm. A possible outlier might be 23 cm.

b. Ask students to make a boxplot. Table 3.4.3 shows the five-number summary for the sample data shown in the frequency table. Figure 3.4.2 displays the boxplot of the sample sixth-grade class data. It is drawn above the dotplot to help in the analysis of the data.

Table 3.4.3 Five-Number Summary of Sample Sixth-Grade Class Data

Min	Q1	Median	Q3	Max
14	16	18	19	23

102

Note that the first quartile is the median of the data points strictly below the overall median of the data set, and the third quartile is the median of the data points strictly above the overall median of the data set.

Length of Shoes

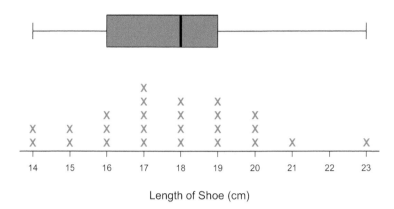

Figure 3.4.2 Boxplot and dotplot of the sample sixth-grade class data

c. Discuss with students how to interpret the boxplot. Students should understand that there are about the same **number of shoes** between the minimum and Q1, Q1 to Q2, Q2 to Q3, and Q3 to the maximum, or approximately 25% of the data in each of these four intervals. Note that Q2 is the median.

d. Demonstrate for your students how to determine if there are any outliers using the following steps:

Find the interquartile range (IQR): IQR = Q3 - Q1 = 19 - 16 = 3.

Multiply 1.5 x IQR = 1.5 x 3 = 4.5.

Add this value to Q3: 19 + 4.5 = 23.5 (called the upper fence) and subtract it from Q1: 16 - 4.5 = 11.5 (called the lower fence).

All data points that fall outside these fences are taken to be outliers.

Note that even though 23 is the highest value and follows a gap in the dotplot (hence a possible outlier), it is not an outlier according to the boxplot IQR rule.

3. The next step in the analysis of the data is to focus on the measures of center.

a. The question your students are investigating is how long a middle-school student's shoe is. For the given data set, one possible answer is

17 cm—the mode—because more students had a shoe length of 17 than any other shoe length.

b. Another answer would be 18 cm—the median—because 18 lies in the middle of the ordered shoe lengths. There are 12 data points to the left of one of the 18s and 12 to its right.

c. Another possibility is the shoe length determined if all the students had the same shoe length. Such a measure is called the arithmetic average, or the mean, and is interpreted as the "fair share" shoe length (i.e., if all 25 students had the same length shoe, that length would be 17.72 cm). If the 25 shoes were lined up toe to heel, the sum of the lengths would be 443 cm. If all 25 shoes were of the same length, they would each have length 443/25 = 17.72 cm. (See Investigation 3.3, "How Expensive Is Your Name," for a development of the fair share sense of mean.)

4. The next step in the analysis of data is to characterize a **spread** of the shoe length distribution.

a. The data cover the interval from the minimum of 14 to the maximum of 23. The length of the interval is the maximum - minimum, or 9 cm. This length is called the **range** of the distribution. (Note that in statistics, the range is a single number. It is tempting to say that the data *range* from 14 to 23 cm, but this would not be a correct interpretation of the statistical term range.)

b. The boxplot suggests another measure of spread, namely the distance between the first and third quartiles, 19 - 16 = 3 cm. This measure, called the **interquartile range,** denoted by **IQR,** provides a measure of spread of the middle 50% of the shoe lengths. (Recall that the first quartile is the median of the data points strictly below the median of the data set and the third quartile is the median of the data points strictly above the median of the data set.)

c. When a distribution is relatively symmetric, the mean is a good measure of center. Another measure of spread is constructed incorporating how far the data are from its mean, on average. The fair share absolute deviation, called the **mean absolute deviation** and denoted by **MAD**, is the arithmetic average of the absolute deviations.

d. The first step to find the mean absolute deviation is to find how far the data are from the mean by subtracting the mean from each shoe length. Table 3.4.4 shows the 25 shoe lengths from the sample sixth-grade class and the deviations the data are from the mean.

e. Ask your students to find the sum of the deviations the data are from the mean. They should find the sum equals 0. Some of the deviations are positive if the data are greater than the mean and negative if the data are less than the mean. This indicates that the mean is the balance point of a set of data placed on a line that balances the total of the positive deviations from it with the total of the negative deviations from it.

f. The next step to finding the mean absolute deviation is to find the absolute value of the deviations. They are in the third column of Table 3.4.4.

g. The final step is to find the mean of the absolute values. **Note:** Squaring the deviations instead of taking absolute values is the basis of another measure of spread, the standard deviation, a high-school topic.

Table 3.4.4 shows the calculations for the deviations from the mean and the absolute deviations from the mean for the sixth-graders' class data set of shoe lengths. For this example, the MAD = 43.28/25 = 1.73 cm (rounded to hundredths). On average (fair share), the shoe lengths are 1.73 cm away from the mean shoe length of 17.72 cm.

Table 3.4.4 Table of Calculations to Find the Mean Absolute Deviation

Shoe Length	Length - Mean	|Length - Mean|	Shoe Length	Length - Mean	|Length - Mean|
20	20 - 17.72 = 2.28	2.28	18	18 - 17.72 = 0.28	0.28
17	17 - 17.72 = -0.72	0.72	15	15 - 17.72 = -2.72	2.72
17	17 - 17.72 = -0.72	0.72	21	21 - 17.72 = 3.28	3.28
19	19 - 17.72 = 1.28	1.28	17	17 - 17.72 = -0.72	0.72
18	18 - 17.72 = 0.28	0.28	14	14 - 17.72 = -3.72	3.72
20	20 - 17.72 = 2.28	2.28	16	16 - 17.72 = -1.72	1.72
17	17 - 17.72 = -0.72	0.72	23	23 - 17.72 = 5.28	5.28
19	19 - 17.72 = 1.28	1.28	16	16 - 17.72 = -1.72	1.72
14	14 - 17.72 = -3.72	3.72	18	18 - 17.72 = 0.28	0.28
17	17 - 17.72 = -0.72	0.72	19	19 - 17.72 = 1.28	1.28
20	20 - 17.72 = 2.28	2.28	16	16 - 17.72 = -1.72	1.72
15	15 - 17.72 = -2.72	2.72	18	18 - 17.72 = 0.28	0.28
19	19 - 17.72 = 1.28	1.28	Sum	0	43.28

Interpret the Results in the Context of the Original Question

Ask your students to write a report that begins with an answer to the original question, "How long is a middle-school student's shoe?" They need to support their answer by focusing on what they found out about the shape, center, and spread of their data. Graphs (dotplot and boxplot) should be included.

Example of 'Interpret the Results'

Note: The following is not an example of actual student work, but an example of all the parts that should be included in student work.

We wanted to know about the lengths of our shoes. From collecting our shoe lengths in a frequency table, we drew the following dotplot and boxplot.

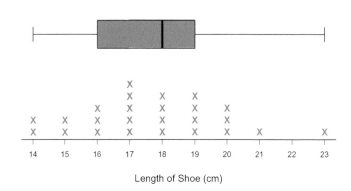

Length of Shoes

Length of Shoe (cm)

It was neat to put the two graphs together to see what one of them showed that the other didn't. For example, the dotplot showed a possible outlier at 23 because of a gap between 21 and 23, but when we did the IQR calculation to detect outliers in a boxplot, 23 was not an outlier.

The dotplot shows the shape of the data to be fairly symmetrical. It's a little hard to see that in the boxplot because the distance from the median to Q3 is short and the distance from Q3 to the max is long. That means 25% of us, or about 6 of us, were close together between the median of 18 and Q3 = 19, but 25% of us, or about 6 of us, were spread out between Q3 = 19 and the max of 23. That's not too symmetric.

Regarding how spread out our shoe lengths are, we calculated three measures of spread. The first is the range, which is the overall distance from the minimum to the maximum, 23 - 14 = 9 cm. The second is the range of the middle 50% of the data. It is called the interquartile range. Its value is the distance from the first quartile to the third quartile, which is 19 - 16 = 3 cm. So, half our shoe lengths occupy an interval of length 3 cm. That's pretty closely packed. The third measure of spread is based on the distance each point is from the mean. This distance in statistics is called a deviation. We discovered that if you calculate all the deviations above the mean, they will be positive and the shoe lengths below the mean will be negative. It was kind of neat to see that when we added them all together, the answer was 0. We now have two meanings for the mean: It's the value everyone would have if everyone were to have the same value and a balance point of the data set put on a line. To find another measure of spread, we took the mean of the absolute values of the deviations and called it MAD—that stands for the mean absolute deviation. It was 1.73 cm for our shoe lengths, which means, on average, all our shoe lengths are 1.73 cm away from the mean shoe length of 17.72 cm.

Our teacher told us that when we get to high school, we will learn another really cool measure of spread that is important and we will be able to understand it because of our working with MAD.

Assessment with Answers

Chris, a seventh-grader, collected the shoe length of a group of 10 students from the eighth grade to investigate the question regarding the shoe length of eighth graders. The data are shown in the following frequency table:

Shoe Length (cm)	16	17	18	19	20
Frequency	1	2	4	2	1

1. Draw a dotplot of the data and describe the shape of the distribution.

Length of Shoes

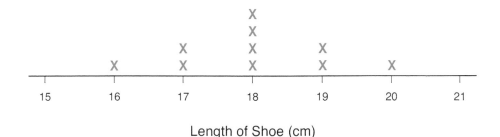

Length of Shoe (cm)

Distribution is mound-shaped and symmetric.

2. Draw a boxplot of the data and describe the spread of the distribution.

Length of Shoes

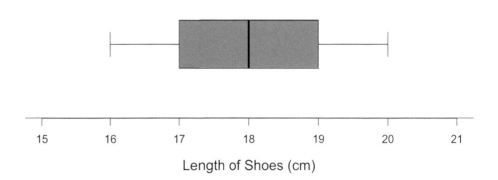

Length of Shoes (cm)

Five-number summary: Min = 16, Q1 = 17, Med = 18, Q3 = 19, Max = 20

3. Find the mean of the data. 18

4. Is the mean a useful measure of center? Yes, since the distribution is mound-shaped and symmetric.

5. Explain how to interpret the mean in this context. If all the students had the same length shoe, the length would be 18 cm.

6. Find the mean absolute deviation of the shoe lengths and interpret it in the context of this problem.

Shoe Length	Deviations from the Mean	Absolute Deviations
16	16 - 18 = -2	2
17	17 - 18 = -1	1
17	17 - 18 = -1	1
18	18 - 18 = 0	0
18	18 - 18 = 0	0
18	18 - 18 = 0	0
18	18 - 18 = 0	0
19	19 - 18 = 1	1
19	19 - 18 = 1	1
20	20 - 18 = 2	2

Sum of the absolute deviations = 8

Mean absolute deviation = 8/10 = .8

On average, the shoe lengths are 0.8 cm from the mean length of 18 cm.

Extensions

1. An alternative approach to developing the mean as a balance point is to have your students look at the dotplot and make a guess as to where a fulcrum should be placed to balance the graph. Suppose their guess for the balance point is 18. The first five rows of a table that shows the deviations of the data from their guess of 18 would be the following:

Table for Calculating Deviations	
Shoe Length	Shoe Length - 18
20	20 - 18 = 2
17	17 - 18 = -1
17	17 - 18 = -1
19	19 - 18 = 1
18	18 - 18 = 0

Using 18 as a guess for the mean, the sum of the deviations of all 25 shoe lengths is -7. A properly placed fulcrum would be one such that the total of the negative deviations balances (cancels out) the total of the positive deviations. Since the sum was -7, the guess for the balance point was too high.

Have the students try 17. The sum of the deviations using 17 as the guess for the mean is 18, which would mean the guess of 17 was too low.

Trying 17.7 produces a total of 0.5. This would mean that 17.7 would be very close to the actual balance point. We know the mean is 17.72, so that if we now tried 17.72, the sum of all 25 deviations would turn out to be 0.

2. Add famous athletes' shoe sizes to your class data. For example, Shaquille O'Neal has shoe size 22 (about 47 cm); Michael Phelps has 14 (about 30.5 cm); and Lebron James is 16 (about 31.8 cm). How are the original conclusions affected by the inclusion of these three data points?

3. Investigate any relationship between shoe length in centimeters and shoe size. From your findings, what would a student's shoe size be if the student has a shoe length of 17 cm?

References

Bereska, C., L. C. Bolster, C. A. Bolster, and R. Scheaffer. 1998. *Exploring statistics in the elementary grades: Book one, grades k–6*. White Plains, NY: Dale Seymour.

Franklin, C., G. Kader, D. Mewborn, J. Moreno, R. Peck, M. Perry, and R. Scheaffer. 2007. *Guidelines for assessment and instruction in statistics education (GAISE) report: A pre-k–12 curriculum framework*. Alexandria, VA: American Statistical Association. *www.amstat.org/education/gaise*.

National Council of Teachers of Mathematics. 2000. *Principles and standards for school mathematics*. Reston, VA: National Council of Teachers of Mathematics.

Common Core State Standards for Mathematics. www.corestandards.org.

COMPARING GROUPS

Investigation 4.1
How Far Can You Jump?

Overview

This investigation focuses on students conducting a **comparative experiment** to explore the effect a fixed target will have on the distance students can jump from a starting line. Students will be randomly assigned to one of two groups. The first group will be asked to jump as far as they can from the starting line with no target in front of them. The second group will be asked to jump as far as they can, but a target (strip of tape) will be placed on the floor in front of them. Students will collect data about the distance jumped by each member of the two groups. They will display the data in a **back-to-back stemplot** or **boxplot**. Analysis of the data will include graphs and calculations of measures of center and spread.

GAISE Components

This investigation follows the four components of statistical problem solving put forth in the *Guidelines for Assessment and Instruction in Statistics Education (GAISE) Report.* The four components are formulate a statistical question that can be answered with data, design and implement a plan to collect appropriate data, analyze the collected data by graphical and numerical methods, and interpret the results of the analysis in the context of the original question. This is a GAISE Level B activity.

Learning Goals

Students will be able to do the following after completing this investigation:

- Conduct an experiment to investigate a question

- Collect data and organize the results in a back-to-back stemplot (Level A) or side-by-side boxplots (Level B)

- Use the data to answer the question posed

Common Core State Standards for Mathematical Practice

1. Make sense of problems and persevere in solving them.
2. Reason abstractly and quantitatively.
3. Construct viable arguments and critique the reasoning of others.

4. Model with mathematics.

6. Attend to precision.

Common Core State Standards
Grade Level Content

6.SP.1 Recognize a statistical question as one that anticipates variability in the data related to the question and accounts for it in the answers.

6.SP.2 Understand that a set of data collected to answer a statistical question has a distribution that can be described by its center, spread, and overall shape.

6.SP.3 Recognize that a measure of center for a numerical data set summarizes all its values with a single number, while a measure of variation describes how its values vary with a single number.

6.SP.4 Display numerical data in plots on a number line, including dotplots, histograms, and boxplots.

6.SP.5 Summarize numerical data sets in relation to their context, such as by the following:

a. Reporting the number of observations

b. Describing the nature of the attribute under investigation, including how it was measured and its units of measurement

c. Giving quantitative measures of center (median and/or mean) and variability (interquartile range and/or mean absolute deviation), as well as describing any overall pattern and any striking deviations from the overall pattern with reference to the context in which the data were gathered

d. Relating the choice of measures of center and variability to the shape of the data distribution and the context in which the data were gathered

NCTM Principles and Standards
for School Mathematics

Data Analysis and Probability

Grades 6–8 Students should find, use, and interpret measures of center and spread—including mean and interquartile range—and discuss and understand the correspondence between data sets and their graphical representations, especially histograms, stemplots, boxplots, and scatterplots.

Materials

- Masking tape
- Meter sticks
- Recording sheets (included on CD)
- Calculators

Estimated Time

1–2 days

Instructional Plan

Note: You may want to involve the physical education teacher in your school for assistance in this activity. This teacher can give suggestions regarding where to set the target line and how to collect the data.

✏ Formulate a Statistical Question

1. Ask your students if they know what a standing long jump is. Has anyone in class done a standing long jump before? Ask one student to demonstrate a standing long jump for the class. (Several short videos demonstrating the standing long jump are available on YouTube.) Share with your students that Norwegian Arne Tvervaag holds the world record for the standing long jump. He jumped 3.71 meters (12' 2.1") on November 11, 1968.

2. Discuss with your students some reasons why one student might jump farther than another. The following are some possible reasons students may come up with: height of a student, boys might jump farther than girls, what shoes they are wearing, whether there is a prize for the longest jump.

3. After students have generated their own ideas, ask them if they think setting a target line might help a student jump farther. This investigation discusses the statistical question, "Will students jump farther if they are given a fixed target in front of them?"

✏ Collect Appropriate Data

1. Before collecting data, there are procedures that need to be discussed with your students. It is important that your students are placed randomly into a group, that each student performs the jump in the same manner, and that the length of each jump is measured in the same way.

2. The generally accepted way to perform the standing long jump is to 1) stand with both feet up to the start line, 2) take a jump forward with both feet as far as you can, and 3) stay on your feet. **Note:** To avoid injury, this is best done on a mat or grass, instead of a hard floor.

3. The length of the jump should be measured from the start line to the part of the body that lands closest to the start line.

4. Ask students how the two groups should be formed. Students might suggest that there should be an equal number of boys and girls in each group, and some students will want to make sure the best athletes in class are spread between both groups. However, these designs do not ensure randomness. It is important that the groups are formed in a random manner. Random selection helps ensures that the two groups are similar in any attributes that might make a difference in performing the standing long jump. Discuss with your students how you might assign them randomly. One way to select students randomly is to write each of their names on an index card and then, after thoroughly mixing, draw one card at a time from the bag. The student named on the first card is assigned to the No Target group; the student named on the second card drawn is assigned to the Target group. Assignment of students continues to alternate until all the names have been drawn.

5. Set up two stations (one with No Target and one with a Target line) on the playground or in the gym where your students will perform the standing long jump. For the Target group, you may wish to ask the physical education teacher approximately how far your students will be able to jump. You want to set the target line toward the upper limit of what most students can jump. A suggestion for 12-year-olds is 200 cm from the start line.

6. Each student in the No Target group will be asked to jump as far as she/ he can from the starting position marked with tape on the floor. Following the jump, with a piece of masking tape, mark the location of the student's heel, or their hand if they fall backward. The heel or hand that is closest to the starting position should be used. Measure the distance in centimeters from the starting point to the end of the jump using a meter stick or extendable tape measure. Record the measurements on the data collection sheet. Similarly, each child in the Target group will be asked to jump as far as she/he can from the starting position marked with tape on the floor. Follow the same procedures as with the No Target group for marking, measuring, and recording the jump.

7. Collect the class data. Display each of the individual student results on the board under the headings No Target group and Target group. An example is shown in Table 4.1.1.

Table 4.1.1 An Example of Data Collected
from a Group of 12-Year-Olds

Length in Centimeters for No Target Group
146 190 109 181 155 167 154 171 157 156 128 157 167 162 137

Length in Centimeters for Target Group
199 167 147 180 185 170 171 139 154 126 179 158 181 152

Note that the statistical design being followed is an independent groups one, in which each student participates in exactly one of the two treatments. Is this the best procedure to follow in the context of this problem? Be sure to read the extension and discuss it with your students after the experiment has been completed.

✏ Analyze the Data

1. With the class data displayed on the board, ask your students if they think one group was able to jump farther than the other. Explain to your students that it is difficult to compare groups by just looking at the numbers; it is helpful to organize the data in a graph.

2. Have your students construct a back-to-back stemplot of the results. See Figure 4.1.1. On the board, label the No Target group on the left and the Target group on the right. The stems of the plot are the numbers 10–19, which represent 100 to 190. The "leaf" in the display represents the ones digit.

Jumping Length

No Target		Stem	Target
	9	10	
		11	
	8	12	6
	7	13	9
	6	14	7
7 6 7 4	5	15	4 8 2
2 7	7	16	7
	1	17	0 1 9
	1	18	0 5 1
	0	19	9

Key: 16|7 represents 167 cm

Figure 4.1.1 Back-to-back stemplot comparing length of jumps for No Target group and Target group

3. Ask your students to modify their back-to-back stemplots showing the data (units digits) ordered. Figure 4.1.2 shows the back-to-back stemplot with the digits in order.

Jumping Length

No Target		Stem	Target
	9	10	
		11	
	8	12	6
	7	13	9
	6	14	7
7 7 6 5	4	15	2 4 8
7 7	2	16	7
	1	17	0 1 9
	1	18	0 1 5
	0	19	9

Key: 16|7 represents 167 cm

Figure 4.1.2 Back-to-back stemplot comparing length of jumps for No Target group and Target group with the digits in order

4. Ask your students to compare the shapes of the two distributions from the stemplots. Note that the jump lengths in the No Target group are

concentrated between 150–170 cm, whereas those in the Target group are spread out a bit more and appear to be higher in length. The shape of the No Target distribution is peaked, while the shape of the Target distribution is more flat, uniform. There is a gap in the No Target group, suggesting that 109 cm might be what is called an *outlier*, an atypical value. The presence of an outlier might influence the most appropriate measure of center for the data set.

5. Ordering the digits in a stemplot is helpful when finding the quartiles (note the median is the second quartile). The three quartiles are used to construct another graph—the boxplot. To construct a boxplot, have your students find the five-number summary—minimum value, first quartile (Q1) that is the median of the data points strictly below the median of the distribution, the median, the third quartile (Q3) that is the median of the data points strictly above the median of the distribution, and the maximum value. Table 4.1.2 shows the five-number summary for both the Target group and No Target group. Figure 4.1.3 shows the side-by-side boxplots for the data in this example.

Table 4.1.2 Five-Number Summary for Target and No Target Group

	Min	Max	Median	Q1	Q3
No Target Group	109	190	157	146	167
Target Group	126	199	168.5	152	180

Jumping Length

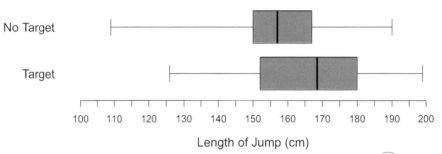

Figure 4.1.3 Side-by-side boxplots comparing length of jumps for No Target group and Target group

6. Remind your students that they are investigating whether a target helps or hinders the length of jumps. Ask your students to discuss several comparisons based on the two boxplots that will contribute to their final answer for the statistical question, "Will students jump farther if they are given a fixed target in front of them?" It is important to have your

students first discuss the meaning of the two boxplots. They should focus on comparing the medians, quartiles, and four sections of the boxplots. Note that in addition to the comparison of shapes they have made, they should note that the median for the Target group is 11.5 cm higher than that for the No Target group. That's a considerable distance. A related note to that comparison of medians is that although the first quartiles are somewhat similar (meaning that 75% of the students in each group jumped at least somewhere around 150 cm), half the students in the Target group jumped more than 168.5 cm, but half the students in the No Target group jumped no more than 157 cm, 11.5 cm shorter. Even more telling is that half the Target group jumped farther than 75% of the No Target group (Target group median is 168.5, No Target group Q3 is 167).

7. In addition to graphing and finding the median and quartiles, ask your students to find another measure of center—the mean length of the jumps. Table 4.1.3 (template available on the CD) shows the sample data and five-number summary and the mean. Discuss with your students whether to use the mean or median. The median is more robust in that it is not influenced by extreme values. The mean is influenced by extreme values, but includes all the information in the calculation. In this example, it appears that 109 is an extreme value in the No Target Group, so the median might be a better measure of center than the mean for the No Target group. Note that whichever measure is used, it should be the same for comparison purposes.

Table 4.1.3 Example Recording Sheet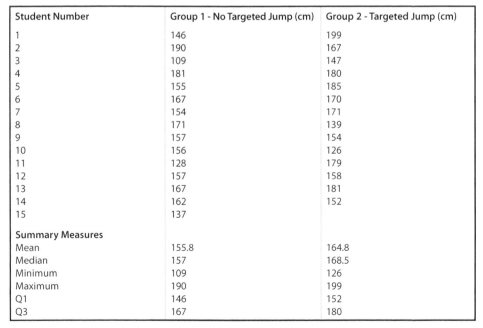

Student Number	Group 1 - No Targeted Jump (cm)	Group 2 - Targeted Jump (cm)
1	146	199
2	190	167
3	109	147
4	181	180
5	155	185
6	167	170
7	154	171
8	171	139
9	157	154
10	156	126
11	128	179
12	157	158
13	167	181
14	162	152
15	137	
Summary Measures		
Mean	155.8	164.8
Median	157	168.5
Minimum	109	126
Maximum	190	199
Q1	146	152
Q3	167	180

8. Statistics is the study of variability, so a measure of spread needs to be computed to better compare the two groups. Discuss with your students that they calculated one measure of variability when they drew their boxplots, the interquartile range (IQR). The IQR = Q3 – Q1, the difference between the 1st quartile and the 3rd quartile. The IQR provides a measure of the spread of the middle 50% of the jump lengths. In the example data, the IQR of the No Target group is 21 and the IQR for the Target group is 28. This means the middle 50% of the jump lengths for the Target group has a greater spread than the middle 50% of the jump lengths for the No Target group. Discuss with your students what conclusion can be drawn about a data set concerning how spread out it is. Note that a compact data set makes its center more believable that it is reflecting the true value, whereas a widely dispersed data set makes us less sure the center is really characterizing typical performance.

Have your students compare the two IQRs in words in the context of the data (i.e., what do the IQRs say about how spread out the jump lengths are in the No Target group compared to the Target group). Have them provide a possible contextual explanation as to why they are different. Suggestions will vary. One possibility is that in the presence of a target, people react differently. Some tense up and others push themselves beyond their normal performance.

9. Recall that from the stemplot for the No Target group, 109 was thought to be a possible outlier because it was separated from the rest of the data by a gap. The boxplot allows for a more formal determination as to whether a value should be labeled an outlier (extreme value). The procedure is to calculate what are called the upper fence and lower fence. Data points outside the fences are considered outliers (i.e., data atypical to the data set). The upper fence is Q3 + 1.5*IQR; the lower fence is Q1 – 1.5*IQR. Ask your students to calculate the fences for the No Target group. Note that the lower fence is Q1 – 1.5*IQR = 146 – 1.5*(167 – 146) = 114.5. So, it can be concluded that 109 is an outlier. The implication of this is that, in a statistical analysis of this No Target data set, it would be advisable to use the median as a measure of its center, rather than the mean.

✐ Interpret the Results in the Context of the Original Question

1. Have your students recall the original question, "Will students jump farther if they are given a fixed target in front of them?" Ask your students to write a summary of the experiment that starts with stating an answer

to the question and then supporting their answer with their analysis. They should focus their summary on using center and spread measures, but also include a discussion about the shapes of the graphs they drew.

2. Have your students describe what they think the distribution of jumps with and without a target would be if 2nd graders performed the experiment. Do they think their conclusion they reached about the effect of a target line will be the same for the 2nd graders?

Example of 'Interpret the Results'

Note: The following is not an example of actual student work, but an example of all the parts that should be included in student work.

We conducted a comparative experiment in which some students did a standing long jump with no target in front of them and others did a standing long jump with a target 200 cm in front of them to answer the statistical question, "Will students jump farther if they are given a fixed target in front of them?" (Our gym teacher suggested 200 cm would be a good target for 12-year-olds.)

To determine which of us would be in the No Target group and which would be the Target group, we put our names in a hat. The first name randomly drawn from the hat was assigned to the No Target group. The second name drawn was assigned to the Target group. We went back and forth like that until everyone had been assigned to a group.

We measured our distances in centimeters from the starting line to where the closer heel of our shoes landed to the start line. (Everyone landed on their feet.) We tried to make sure everyone did the jump the same way to avoid introducing any sort of bias, like measurement bias, into our results. We drew two comparative graphs of our data.

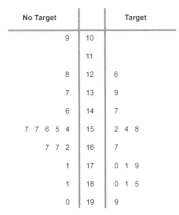

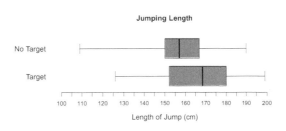

Key: 16|7 represents 167 cm

From the stemplot—except for one possible outlier (109) in the No Target group, it looked like the data sets were spread about the same. But the IQR for the No Target group is 21 and a larger 28 for the Target group, so the middle 50% of the No Target group data is more compact than for the Target group.

Actually, it's better for a data set to have a small variation because it makes us more confident about the centering value. We thought the target group should be more compact because those jumpers had something to concentrate on, but it didn't turn out that way. Regarding the 109, it is an outlier looking at the gap in the stemplot, and it is also an outlier using the Q1 - 1.5*IQR rule for the boxplot. Any value below 146 – 1.5 * (167 – 146) = 114.5 is considered an outlier.

So, did those in the Target group jump farther than the No Target group? From the stemplots, the Target group is shifted to the right compared to the No Target group. Because the No Target group has an outlier, we decided to compare the two groups with medians, rather than means. Based on medians, the answer would be yes, since the median for the Target group was 168.5 cm compared to the median for the No Target group of 157 cm. The Target group jumped a full 11.5 cm longer. In fact, half (seven students) of the Target group jumped farther than 168 cm, but only 3 of the 15 No Target group (20%) jumped that far. Having a target produces higher standing long jump distances. We were wondering if the same conclusion would be made for other age groups. Our guess is that no matter what age groups do this experiment, the results will be similar, since it seems better to have a target as a goal to achieve.

Assessment with Answers

A group of students conducted an experiment to compare the effect of where the target line is placed for the standing long jump. Target lines were placed at 100 cm and 300 cm. Table 4.1.4 shows the length of the jumps in cm for each group.

Table 4.1.4 Jump Lengths (cm) for Groups with Target of 100 cm and 300 cm

100 cm Target	149	141	161	114	116	142	129	149	138	158	145
300 cm Target	168	185	194	167	147	151	169	178	167	166	139

1. Does the distance a target line is from the start line affect the distance students jump in the standing long jump? Yes, students tended to jump farther when the target line was set at 300 cm.

2. Use words, numbers, and graphs to justify your answer by using at least one graph, a measure of center, and a measure of spread.

Summary

	100 cm target	300 cm target
Mean	140.2	166.5
Minimum	114	139
Q1	129	151
Median	142	167
Q3	149	178
Maximum	161	194
IQR	20	27

Jumping Length

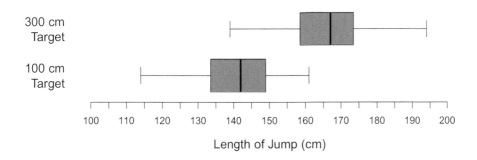

Students tended to jump farther when the target line was set at 300 cm than at 100 cm. The mean jumping distance for the 300 cm target was 166.5 cm, while the mean for the 100 cm target was 140.2. The boxplot of the 300 cm target group is shifted much further right than the 100 cm target group. About 75% of the data in the 300 cm target group are greater than about 75% of the 100 cm group.

Extensions

1. As mentioned earlier, the procedure used with all students knowing the experimental condition will no doubt bias the results, as those not assigned to the Target group may imagine a target line. To avoid this potential introduction of bias into the model, redesign the experiment using a **matched pairs** design. Each student does the standing long jump at both stations and the difference—target jump distance minus the no target jump distance—is noted between the two jumps. Your students

should be assigned randomly to which jump they do first. Your students will analyze the differences by making a dotplot, stemplot, or boxplot. If the differences are generally greater than zero, then target jump distances were better than no target distances.

2. Another measure of spread is the mean absolute deviation (MAD), found in Common Core Standard 6.SP.5c (see Investigation 3.4). Calculate the mean absolute deviation (MAD) for each group and compare the two MADs in words in the context of the experiment.

The MAD is the average of the absolute values of the distances from the group's mean. "Deviation" refers to the difference a value is from the mean. "Absolute deviation" is the absolute value of that difference. Column one of Table 4.1.5 contains the data; column two lists the data minus the mean (the deviation); and column three has the absolute value of the deviations in column two. To find the MAD, find the mean of the values in column three.

Table 4.1.5

No Target	No Target – Mean	|No Target – Mean|
146	146 - 155.8 = -9.8	9.8
190	190 - 155.8 = 34.2	34.2
109	109 - 155.8 = -46.8	46.8
181	181 - 155.8 = 25.2	25.2
155	155 - 155.8 = -0.8	0.8
167	167 - 155.8 = 11.2	11.2
154	154 - 155.8 = -1.8	1.8
171	171 - 155.8 = 15.2	15.2
157	157 - 155.8 = 1.2	1.2
156	156 - 155.8 = 0.2	0.2
128	128 - 155.8 = -27.8	27.8
157	157 - 155.8 = 1.2	1.2
167	167 - 155.8 = 11.2	11.2
162	162 - 155.8 = 6.2	6.2
137	137 - 155.8 = -18.8	18.8

The sum of the absolute deviations in this example for the no target data is the sum of the third column, namely 211.6. Dividing the sum by the number of values, 15, yields the mean of 14.1. In words, the average distance away from 155.8 cm that the 15 students jumped was 14.1 cm for the no target group.

Similarly, the MAD for the target group is 16.2 cm. So, according to the point of view of average distance data are from its mean, the target data are spread out more from their mean than the no target data are from their mean. Ask your students if that result is reflected in their boxplots. Why?

References

Franklin, C., G. Kader, D. Mewborn, J. Moreno, R. Peck, M. Perry, and R. Scheaffer. 2007. *Guidelines for assessment and instruction in statistics education (GAISE) report: A pre-k–12 curriculum framework*. Alexandria, VA: American Statistical Association. *www.amstat.org/education/gaise*.

National Council of Teachers of Mathematics. 2000. *Principles and standards for school mathematics*. Reston, VA: National Council of Teachers of Mathematics.

Common Core State Standards for Mathematics. www.corestandards.org.

INVESTIGATION 4.2
HOW FAST CAN YOU SORT CARDS?

Overview

Students are always interested in how fast they can do something such as playing video games, texting, or running a race. This investigation focuses on the use of a comparative experiment to investigate possible differences in the average time it takes a student to sort a set of 10 cards in numerical order when the size (number of digits) in the numbers varies. Students will be **randomly assigned** to one of three groups. Students in Group 1 will each sort a deck of cards labeled with two-digit numbers. Students in Group 2 will each sort a deck of cards labeled with three-digit numbers. Students in Group 3 will each sort a deck of cards labeled with four-digit numbers. A stopwatch will be used to measure the time needed to complete the task. Students will compare the summary from each group using **measures of center** (mean and median) and **variability** (range, interquartile range, mean absolute deviation) and graphically compare the results using stemplots and boxplots. An informal inference procedure will be introduced as suggested by the Common Core State Standards. This investigation is focused on providing an answer to "Does the time it takes to sort a deck of digit cards vary with the number of digits in the numbers?"

GAISE Components

This investigation follows the four components of statistical problem solving put forth in the *Guidelines for Assessment and Instruction in Statistics Education (GAISE) Report*. The four components are formulate a statistical question that can be answered with data, design and implement a plan to collect appropriate data, analyze the collected data by graphical and numerical methods, and interpret the results of the analysis in the context of the original question. This is a GAISE Level B activity.

Learning Goals

Students will be able to do the following after completing this investigation:

- Formulate questions that can be addressed with data and collect, organize, and display relevant data to answer them

- Explain the idea and use of random assignment

- Conduct an experiment to investigate questions

- Use the data to answer the questions posed

- Collect data and organize the results into stemplots and boxplots

- Compare the results from each group using summary measures of center (such as mean and median) and measures of variability (such as range and interquartile range)

Common Core State Standards for Mathematical Practice

1. Make sense of problems and persevere in solving them.
2. Reason abstractly and quantitatively.
3. Construct viable arguments and critique the reasoning of others.
4. Model with mathematics.

Common Core State Standards Grade Level Content

6.SP.1 Recognize a statistical question as one that anticipates variability in the data related to the question and accounts for it in the answers.

6.SP.2 Understand that a set of data collected to answer a statistical question has a distribution that can be described by its center, spread, and overall shape.

6.SP.3 Recognize that a measure of center for a numerical data set summarizes all its values with a single number, while a measure of variation describes how its values vary with a single number.

6.SP.4 Display numerical data in plots on a number line, including dotplots, histograms, and boxplots.

6.SP.5 Summarize numerical data sets in relation to their context, such as by the following:

a. Reporting the number of observations

b. Describing the nature of the attribute under investigation, including how it was measured and its units of measurement

c. Giving quantitative measures of center (median and/or mean) and variability (interquartile range and/or mean absolute deviation), as well as describing any overall pattern and any striking deviations from the overall pattern with reference to the context in which the data were gathered.

   d. Relating the choice of measures of center and variability to the shape of the data distribution and the context in which the data were gathered.

7.SP.3 Informally assess the degree of visual overlap of two numerical data distributions with similar variabilities measuring the difference between the centers by expressing it as a multiple of a measure of variability.

NCTM Principles and Standards for School Mathematics

Data Analysis and Probability

Grades 6–8 In grades 6–8, all students should find, use, and interpret measures of center and spread—including mean and interquartile range—and discuss and understand the correspondence between data sets and their graphical representations, especially histograms, stemplots, boxplots, and scatterplots.

Materials

- Three sets of numbered cards (template available on the CD)
- Recording sheets (available on the CD)
- Stopwatches or other timing devices (need to be able to time to nearest 1/10 of a second)

Estimated Time

1–2 days

Instructional Plan

✏ **Formulate a Statistical Question**

1. Begin the investigation by asking your students when they sort items and what items they sort. Ask if they ever sort numbers in their mathematics class. When finding the median of a set of data, the data must be arranged in order. Tell your students this investigation focuses on sorting cards with numbers on them. Explain that one deck consists of two-digit

numbers, a second with three-digit numbers, and a third with four-digit numbers. Show your students one of these decks of cards. Ask them for factors that may influence how fast they can sort the cards from lowest to highest. They may suggest factors such as the size of the numbers (i.e., the number of digits in the number), the underlying sequence of the numbers, the number of cards, and any incentive offered such as whether there is a prize for the fastest time.

2. Help your students write their suggested factors in the form of a statistical question. This investigation addresses the statistical question, "Does the time it takes to sort a deck of digit cards vary with the number of digits in the numbers?"

✏ Collect Appropriate Data

1. Introduce the idea of comparing the results from three groups of students, each group doing a different version of the task. This is an example of an experiment.

2. Ask students what the variables are in this investigation. Students should realize the first variable of interest is the experimental group (two, three, or four digits) and the second variable of interest is the amount of time needed to complete the task of sorting the cards (as measured in seconds).

3. Discuss with your students the methods they use to select teams on the playground. Are the methods fair? Does each student have the same chance (opportunity) to be selected? What method should we use to assign students to each of the three groups? One way to select students randomly is to write each of their names on an index card and then, after thoroughly mixing, draw one card out of a bag at a time. The student named on the first card is assigned to the Deck 1 Group; the student named on the second card drawn is assigned to the Deck 2 Group; the student named on the third card drawn is assigned to the Deck 3 Group. Assignment of students continues in this pattern until all the names have been drawn.

   Note that some students may suggest that each student roll a die. If a 1 or 2 comes up, the student uses deck 1; 3 or 4, deck 2; 5 or 6, deck 3. Ask them why this method is not desirable. (We should have about the same number of students assigned to the three decks, but it is possible that, in the extreme, all students roll a 5 or 6, say, using this die method.)

4. Point out that in order for them to truly be able to make comparisons, they need to make sure time is measured in the same way for all participants. Therefore, they all need to use the same type of stopwatch and give careful attention to the beginning and ending of the task. Note that one person should do the timing for each student in the specific group (i.e., two-digit, three-digit, or four-digit) to avoid some of the measurement variability.

5. Within each of the three groups, select a member of the group to serve as the timer (leader). Students will perform the sorting task one at a time within each group. Before each student in the group begins, the leader will shuffle the deck of cards (template of cards available on the CD), hand them to a student, and say "GO" and start the stopwatch. The student will sort the cards in ascending order from lowest to highest and say "DONE" when completed. At that time, the leader will stop the stopwatch and record the time on the data collection form.

6. If a student sorts the numbers in the wrong order, the timer should not stop the watch until the numbers are in the correct order from lowest to highest.

7. Collect the class data on the data collection sheet. See Table 4.2.1 for an example.

Table 4.2.1 Example of Class Data

Time (sec) to Sort 2 Digits	Time (sec) to Sort 3 Digits	Time (sec) to Sort 4 Digits
20.6	26.2	31.2
22.9	25.8	28.6
20.9	24.1	28.3
22.2	24.3	31.3
25.6	25.9	26.8
23.1	24.4	27.9
19.6	26.4	28.9
23.6	29.5	27.2
20.5	28.4	34.3
22.0	25.1	26.2
21.8	24.0	25.2

✏ Analyze the Data

1. Begin the analysis by having your students make observations about the class data such as almost all of the data are between 20–30 seconds.

2. Suggest to your students that more observations can be made from graphs. Have your students make a stemplot of each of the three sets of times. See Figures 4.2.1, 4.2.2, and 4.2.3 for examples.

Sort Times for 2-Digit Numbers

```
19 | 6
20 | 5  6  9
21 | 8
22 | 0  2  9
23 | 1  6
24 |
25 | 6
```

Key: 25|6 represents 25.6 sec.

Figure 4.2.1 Stemplot of sort times for 2-digit numbers

Sort Times for 3-Digit Numbers

```
24 | 0  1  3  4
25 | 1  8  9
26 | 2  4
27 |
28 | 4
29 | 5
```

Key: 26|2 represents 26.2 sec.

Figure 4.2.2 Stemplot of sort times for 3-digit numbers

Sort Times for 4-Digit Numbers

```
25 | 2
26 | 2  8
27 | 2  9
28 | 3  6  9
29 |
30 |
31 | 2  3
32 |
33 |
34 | 3
```

Key: 31|2 represents 31.2 sec.

Figure 4.2.3 Stemplot of sort times for 4-digit numbers

3. Ask your students for some observations from the plots regarding the effect the number of digits has on the time to do the ordering task. Note that they should compare shapes: 2-digit might be characterized as bi-modal, 3-digit as "ski-sloped" skewed to the right, and 4-digit as kind of mound-shaped but with big gaps. Each graph shows gaps, but especially 4-digit. Students have to be careful in that the scales of the stemplots are not the same. Drawing dotplots on the same scale would definitely show that 2-digit is to the left of the other two, with 4-digit drifting to the right. The gaps indicate the presence of potential extreme values called outliers. Outliers need to be identified because they can influence conclusions made about the data set, particularly regarding the center.

4. Discuss with your students methods to summarize the center of a distribution (i.e., what could be a representative time needed to complete the sorting task in each group?). Students should suggest that they could use either the mean or the median. Have them do the calculations and then discuss if one measure is more representative of the center of the data in each group than the other and why they think that way. Note that, for these data sets, the respective medians are 22.0, 25.8, and 28.3; the respective (rounded) means are 22.1, 25.8, and 28.7. The medians and means are very close to each other in each group, so either could be used to measure center. Note that the presence of potential outliers in the data sets did not influence the mean as is often the case. Ask your students to look at each data set to see why the medians and means were comparable.

5. Ask your students to comment on what the means or medians are telling them about the typical time taken to complete the task in each group. Note that it's clear the two-digit group is, on average, the quickest, followed by the three-digit group and the four-digit group coming in the slowest.

6. Ask your students whether the overall distributions are the same since their means and medians are about the same in each case. Discuss with them that distributions are compared by their centers and variability. Discuss ways to measure the variability in the data. The range is a basic measure of spread. Recall that the range is the maximum value minus the minimum value. For these data, respectively, the ranges are 6.0, 5.5, and 9.1. Have your students discuss that the first two groups are somewhat similar in how spread out their data are, whereas the third group contains considerably more spread. Looking at the actual data in the stemplots,

discuss gaps and the reason the spread in the third group is so wide. Note that it is due to 34.3 being so much higher than the rest of the group.

7. Another measure of variation is the interquartile range (IQR) that is the third quartile (Q3) minus the first quartile (Q1). Recall that Q1 is the median of the data points strictly below the median of the distribution. Q3 is the median of the data points strictly above the median of the distribution. Note that the IQR focuses on the middle 50% of a distribution, whereas the range measures the entire distribution from lowest to highest. Have your students calculate Q1, Q3, and the IQR for each group. Referring to the IQRs, discuss how the variations in the groups compare. Also, discuss how conclusions about variation might differ depending on whether the IQR or the range is used. See Table 4.2.2 for a summary of the calculations.

Table 4.2.2 Summary Measures for Each Group

	Min	Max	Range	Q1	Q3	IQR
Two-Digit Group	19.6	25.6	6.0	20.6	23.1	2.5
Three-Digit Group	24.0	29.5	5.5	24.3	26.4	2.1
Four-Digit Group	25.2	34.3	9.1	26.8	31.2	4.4

8. Have students construct side-by-side boxplots. See Figure 4.2.4.

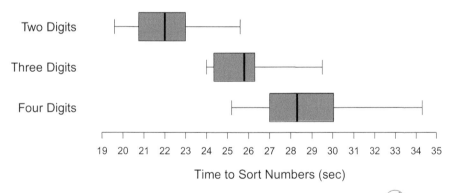

Figure 4.2.4 Side-by-side boxplots of the example class data

9. Ask your students what observations they can make from the boxplots. In particular, is their median measure of center reflected in the boxplots as well as their measures of spread, range, and interquartile range? Discuss how. Note that the boxplots make it clear that the medians are increasing, that the IQR in 2-digit and 3-digit are similar, and that IQR

for 4-digit is about twice as much. All the 3-digit and 4-digit values were higher than 75% of the 2-digit. Seventy-five percent of the 4-digit were higher than 75% of the 3-digit. The 3-digit median exceeded all the 2-digit times.

10. Have your students look at the two types of graphs they have constructed—stemplots and boxplots—and discuss what each of the plots reveal and don't reveal about the comparison of the groups. Lead them to the discovery that several types of graphs should be displayed in a statistical investigation, since each looks at a set of data from a different point of view. Putting all the information together enables the viewer to get a more complete understanding of the experimental results. For example, ask your students if the potential outliers as indicated by the gaps in the stemplots are evident in the boxplots. In boxplots, to identify potential outliers, two calculations need to be made. They are called the lower fence and the upper fence. Values in the data set outside the fences are identified as outliers. The lower fence is $Q1 - 1.5*IQR$, and the upper fence is $Q3 + 1.5*IQR$. Have your students calculate the fences for each data set and determine if there are any outliers according to this rule. There are none.

Group	Q1	Q3	IQR	1.5*IQR	Lower Fence	Upper Fence	Outliers
2-digit	20.6	23.1	2.5	3.75	16.85	26.85	None
3-digit	24.3	26.4	2.1	3.15	21.15	29.55	None
4-digit	26.8	31.2	4.4	6.60	20.20	37.80	None

11. In statistical inference, to determine if the centering points of two distributions are statistically close or far apart, their difference is written in terms of the number of units of some measure of variation. Then, that number of units is determined by various techniques to conclude whether the difference of means is small or large (statistically significant). There is a technique your students will be doing as part of the Common Core State Standard in statistics and probability for all high-school students. (There is a formal technique that students who take Advanced Placement Statistics will learn.)

The Common Core State Standard 7.SP.3 introduces middle-school students to an informal inference procedure by having them measure how far apart two medians are in terms of the number of units of a measure of variability such as IQR. The two distributions being compared have to be of similar variability, and it is the common value that is used to measure how far apart the centers are. Have your students compare the 2-digit and 3-digit distributions. Recall that the median of the 2-digit data set is 22.0 sec and the median of the 3-digit data set is 25.8 sec. The two IQRs are 2.5 and 2.1, which are fairly close. Let's be conservative and take the maximum 2.5 to represent the common spread of the two distributions. By how many IQRs of 2.5 sec do the medians 22.0 and 25.8 differ? The medians of the 2-digit and 3-digit data sets differ by (25.8 − 22.0) / 2.5= 1.5 IQRs.

✎ Interpret the Results in the Context of the Original Question

Have your students recall the original question, "Does the time it takes for a deck of digit cards to be sorted vary with the number of digits in the numbers?" Have your students write a summary of the experiment based on the data collected and analyzed that answers the original question (i.e., what group do they think sorted the cards the fastest and why). They need to support their answer by including the following:

a. A discussion of the plan they used to collect the data

b. The graphs they drew and conclusions made from looking at them

c. The measures of center and variability they computed

d. What the measures said about the comparison of the groups (e.g., whether the measures were similar from group to group).

Example of 'Interpret the Results'

Note: The following is not an example of actual student work, but an example of all the parts that should be included in student work.

We investigated how fast it took us to sort cards that had two-, three-, or four-digit numbers on them. There were 17 cards in each group. We were assigned to one of the groups. To avoid introducing bias into the experimental procedure, we put all our names in a container and then drew them out randomly, one at a time, assigning the first name to the two-digit group, the second to the three-digit group, and the third to the four-digit group. We repeated this until everyone was assigned. After getting our data, we drew stemplots and boxplots.

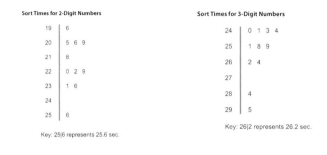

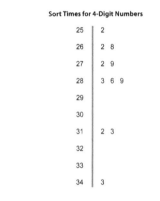

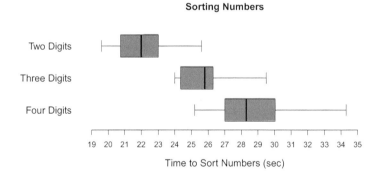

Each stemplot had at least one gap, indicating there were possible outliers. The two-digit shape had a dip in the middle, but looked symmetric. The three-digit shape was definitely skewed to the right. The four-digit one looked like a triangle for the lower values and then had a couple big gaps. We should have put the stemplots side by side on the same scale like we did with the boxplots. It was really clear from the boxplots that the medians increased and the spread of the middle 50% measured by IQR of the 2-digit and 3-digit data sets was similar, with the spread of the 4-digit about twice as much. We saw many comparisons such as all the 3-digit and 4-digit times were longer than 75% of the 2-digit times. The median of 3-digit exceeded all 2-digit. So, overall, it was clear that the times to sort the cards are longer as the number of digits in the numbers increases.

It was interesting that the medians (22.0, 25.8, and 28.3) were about the same as the means (22.1, 25.8, 28.7) even though the distributions had all those gaps. We guessed the possible outliers kind of balanced out the distributions. We checked to see if the outliers we saw in the stemplots were also outliers by the 1.5*IQR calculation for boxplots and none were. Different graphs illustrate different things. Finally, we compared the medians of the 2-digit and 3-digit groups by calculating how many common IQRs separated them. We used the maximum IQR of 2.5 for the value of the IQRs and saw that the medians 22.0 and 25.8 differed by (25.8 − 22.0)/2.5 = 1.5 IQRs. We don't really have a number to compare 1.5 to, but it seems to us that 1.5 IQRs is large enough to say the means differ from each other, since they are really separated when we look at the boxplots.

Assessment with Answers

A class of sixth-grade students conducted an experiment involving LEGO blocks to compare the effect of the type of directions provided to a student on the time needed to complete a task. The task was to build a tower from a given set of blocks. A bag of LEGO blocks contained one of the following three sets of directions:

Directions Set 1: Construct a tower using all the blocks in this bag. The longest blocks should be on the bottom and go up in order to the shortest LEGO blocks at the top.

Directions Set 2: Construct a tower using all the blocks in this bag according to the picture. (Figure 4.2.5)

Directions Set 3: Build a tower with the blocks.

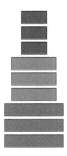

Figure 4.2.5 Diagram shown on directions for set 2

The class was randomly divided into three groups; the results of the experiment are shown in table 4.2.3.

Table 4.2.3 Time to Build Tower

Time (sec) to Build Tower with Directions for Set 1	Time (sec) to Build Tower with Directions for Set 2	Time (sec) to Build Tower with Directions for Set 3
18.1	22.1	11.6
17.5	21.3	15.5
16.3	18.9	15.4
18.8	19.5	15.6
16.2	20.1	15.3
16.0	21.0	15.7
16.6	19.4	13.8
14.8	16.5	16.1
18.1	22.7	15.9
19.8	19.1	16.8
17.6	21.6	14.3
16.5	20.0	12.9
16.7	20.0	17.0

1. What is an appropriate statistical question in the context of this study?
    Does the average time it takes to build a tower with blocks vary with the type of directions given?

2. Find the mean for each group. Set 1 mean = 17.1 sec. Set 2 mean = 20.2 sec. Set 3 mean = 15.1 sec.

3. Find the five-number summary for each of the groups.

	Set 1	Set 2	Set 3
Minimum	14.8	16.5	11.6
Q1	16.3	19.3	14.1
Median	16.7	20.0	15.5
Q3	18.1	21.5	16.0
Maximum	19.8	22.7	17.0

4. Construct side-by-side boxplots of the three groups.

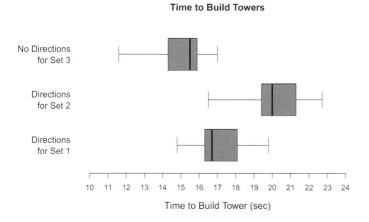

Time to Build Towers

5. Which of the three groups was able to build the tower faster? Using
    words, numbers, and graphs, explain why you chose the group you did.
    Group 3 was able to build the tower the fastest. The median of this group is less
    than the other two. About 75% of the times for Group 3 are less than all of Group 2
    times and 75% of Group 1.

Extension

1. Vary the background of the cards. Using a standard deck of playing cards,
    create three stacks. Each stack contains the cards ace to 10 with one stack
    having cards that are all of the same suit, one stack having cards from the
    two black suits, and one stack having mixed red and black suits. Students
    would investigate the statistical question, "Does the mixture of suits of
    cards relate to the amount of time needed to place the cards in order?"

2. Consider Step 11 of the Analysis of the original question in this inves-
    tigation. Instead of calculating how many common IQRs separate two
    medians, the separation between means also can be calculated in terms
    of MADs. Note that the MADs for each group have to close in value so
    a common value can be determined. Ask your students to calculate mean
    absolute deviations for the three groups to see if any are similar and, if so,
    to do Step 11 using MAD in place of IQR.

References

Franklin, C., G. Kader, D. Mewborn, J. Moreno, R. Peck, M. Perry, and R. Scheaffer. 2007. *Guidelines for assessment and instruction in statistics education (GAISE) report: A pre-k–12 curriculum framework*. Alexandria, VA: American Statistical Association. *www.amstat.org/education/gaise*.

National Council of Teachers of Mathematics. 2000. *Principles and standards for school mathematics*. Reston, VA: National Council of Teachers of Mathematics.

Common Core State Standards for Mathematics. www.corestandards.org.

INVESTIGATION 4.3
HOW HIGH DOES A BALL BOUNCE?

Overview

This investigation focuses on students conducting an experiment to determine the bounce height two kinds of balls will reach when dropped from various heights. Students will collect data using a tennis ball and a golf ball that will be dropped from 30, 60, and 90 cm. They will display the data in a **scatterplot** and interpret the results to answer the statistical question, "Does the height from which a ball is dropped affect how high it bounces?"

Note: The Common Core State Standards do not specifically address measurement error, but this experiment has many areas in which error can occur and that can lead to increased variability within height groups. It could be a topic of extended discussion.

GAISE Components

This investigation follows the four components of statistical problem solving put forth in the *Guidelines for Assessment and Instruction in Statistics Education (GAISE) Report*. The four components are formulate a statistical question that can be answered with data, design and implement a plan to collect appropriate data, analyze the collected data by graphical and numerical methods, and interpret the results of the analysis in the context of the original question. This is a GAISE Level B activity.

Learning Goals

Students will be able to do the following after completing this investigation:

- Pose investigative questions

- Design and conduct an experiment to investigate questions

- Collect data by conducting an experiment and organize the results in a scatterplot

- Recognize linear relationships and use that information to interpret the data

Common Core State Standards for Mathematical Practice

1. Make sense of problems and persevere in solving them.
2. Reason abstractly and quantitatively.
3. Construct viable arguments and critique the reasoning of others.
4. Model with mathematics.
6. Attend to precision.

Common Core State Standards Grade Level Content

6.SP.1 Recognize a statistical question as one that anticipates variability in the data related to the question and accounts for it in the answers.

6.SP.5 Summarize numerical data sets in relation to their context, such as by doing the following:

   a. Reporting the number of observations

    b. Describing the nature of the attribute under investigation, including how it was measured and its units of measurement

     c. Giving quantitative measures of center (median and/or mean) and variability (interquartile range and/or mean absolute deviation), as well as describing any overall pattern and any striking deviations from the overall pattern with reference to the context in which the data were gathered.

     d. Relating the choice of measures of center and variability to the shape of the data distribution and the context in which the data were gathered.

8.SP.1 Construct and interpret scatterplots for bivariate measurement data to investigate patterns of association between two quantities. Describe patterns such as clustering, outliers, positive or negative association, linear association, and nonlinear association.

6.RP.1 Understand the concept of a ratio and use ratio language to describe a ratio relationship between two quantities.

NCTM Principles and Standards for School Mathematics

Data Analysis and Probability

Grades 6–8 All students should find, use, and interpret measures of center and spread—including mean and interquartile range—and discuss and understand the correspondence between data sets and their graphical representations, especially histograms, stemplots, boxplots, and scatterplots.

Materials

- Two types of balls that bounce well (e.g., tennis ball, golf ball, basketball, or table tennis ball)

- Meter sticks

- Calculators

- Recording sheet for each type of ball (available on the CD)

- Graph paper

Estimated Time

Two days

Instructional Plan

✏️ Formulate a Statistical Question

Note: This investigation will use a tennis ball and golf ball, but any two types of balls can be used.

Begin by holding a tennis ball and golf ball up for the students. Have them generate questions about the differences between a tennis ball and golf ball. The following are some of the questions students may come up with:

How are they made?

Which one weighs more?

What are they made out of?

Which ball could you throw farther?

Which ball bounces higher?

Have students generate their own statistical questions. This investigation focuses on two questions: "Does the height from which a ball is dropped affect how high it bounces?" and "Do tennis balls bounce higher, lower, or the same as golf balls?"

✏️ Collect Appropriate Data

1. Ask your students how they think the data should be collected.

2. Point out that to make comparisons, dropping balls must be done in the same way and onto the same type of surface (i.e., experimental conditions must be the same).

3. Following is the procedure for the experiment:

   a. Divide your students into groups of three. One person will drop the ball, a second will observe the height of the bounce, and a third will record the results in a table. Discuss why it would be beneficial to have the same student doing all the ball bouncing and the same student doing the measuring for all heights.

   b. Tape the meter stick to the wall with the 1 cm end on the floor and the 100 cm end at the top.

   c. Hold the tennis ball so that the bottom of the ball is at the 30 cm mark. Drop the ball; don't "throw" the ball down.

   d. Watch carefully to see how high it bounces back up. Record the height in Table 4.3.1. Repeat the drop two more times, recording each trial. Note that students may find it difficult to gauge the height accurately. The ball bounces back very fast. You may want to have two students watch the height of the bounce and compare their numbers. They need to agree or the drop is repeated.

   e. Next, drop the tennis ball from 60 cm three times. Record the height of each of the three bounces in Table 4.3.1. Repeat for a 90 cm height.

Table 4.3.1 Tennis Ball Recording Sheet 💿

	Tennis Ball		
	30 cm	60 cm	90 cm
Trial 1			
Trial 2			
Trial 3			

4. Repeat the tennis ball procedure with a golf ball. Drop a golf ball three times from 30, 60, and 90 cm. Each time, record the height of the bounce. Record the data in a table similar to Table 4.3.2.

Table 4.3.2 Golf Ball Recording Sheet

	Golf Ball		
	30 cm	60 cm	90 cm
Trial 1			
Trial 2			
Trial 3			

5. Tables 4.3.3 and 4.3.4 contain data collected by a group of students.

Table 4.3.3 Example of Tennis Ball Bounce Height

	Tennis Ball		
	30 cm	60 cm	90 cm
Trial 1	16 cm	33 cm	50 cm
Trial 2	17 cm	32 cm	49 cm
Trial 3	16 cm	33 cm	49 cm

Table 4.3.4 Example of Golf Ball Bounce Height

	Golf Ball		
	30 cm	60 cm	90 cm
Trial 1	19 cm	37 cm	55 cm
Trial 2	17 cm	32 cm	49 cm
Trial 3	16 cm	33 cm	49 cm

6. Ask your students what the variables are in this investigation. Students should realize that the first variable of interest is the type of ball (tennis versus golf ball) and the second variable of interest is the height of drop (30, 60, 90 cm).

7. Ask your students why they think they had to drop the balls from each height three times? Students should realize that by taking more measurements, the final heights could be more accurate.

✏️ Analyze the Data

1. Ask your students how the information gathered for each ball at each height can be consolidated. For example, we dropped the tennis ball from 30 cm three times. How can we determine a representative height for the bounce of the tennis ball from 30 cm? Students should suggest that they could use either the mean or the median.

2. Discuss with your students whether to use the mean or median. The median is more robust in that it is less influenced by extreme values. The mean is influenced by extreme values, but includes all the information in a calculation. Students should realize that both measures of center might be valuable here.

3. Have your students calculate the mean for their three drops for each ball at each height. Have them find the median for their three drops for each ball at each height. Students should record the mean and median on their recording sheet. Table 4.3.5 and Table 4.3.6 show results from an example experiment.

Table 4.3.5 Sample Results for Tennis Ball Drop

	Tennis Ball		
	30 cm	60 cm	90 cm
Trial 1	16.0 cm	33.0 cm	50.0 cm
Trial 2	17.0 cm	32.0 cm	49.0 cm
Trial 3	16.0 cm	33.0 cm	49.0 cm
Mean	16.3 cm	32.6 cm	49.3 cm
Median	16.0 cm	33.0 cm	49.0 cm

Table 4.3.6 Sample Results for Golf Ball Drop

	Golf Ball		
	30 cm	60 cm	90 cm
Trial 1	19.0 cm	37.0 cm	55.0 cm
Trial 2	18.0 cm	38.0 cm	57.0 cm
Trial 3	19.0 cm	38.0 cm	56.0 cm
Mean	18.6 cm	37.6 cm	56.0 cm
Median	19.0 cm	38.0 cm	56.0 cm

4. Have each group of students construct a scatterplot of their results. Note that it is customary to put the independent variable on the x-axis, which is the height of the drop for this experiment. The variable on the y-axis should be the height of the bounce (since this is the dependent variable—dependent upon the height of the drop). Instruct your students to graph the median bounce height for each drop height. They should graph the data for both types of balls by using two colors or symbols. See Figure 4.3.1 for an example of a scatterplot of the sample results. **Note:** It might be valuable to graph the raw data and the median. Since there are only three trials, it would provide a nice visual connection of where the median fits into the raw data and how variable the original data are.

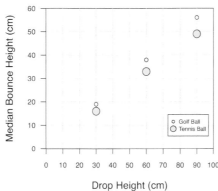

Figure 4.3.1 Scatterplot of median bounce height versus drop height
for a tennis ball and golf ball

5. Ask your students to describe any patterns they observe in their scatterplots. Students should be able to use words such as positive or negative relationship. A positive relationship means that data points go from the lower left of a scatterplot to the upper right, whereas a negative relationship means the data points go from the upper left of a scatterplot to the lower right.

6. Ask your students to calculate the ratio of the bounce height to the drop height for each drop height and for both balls. Record the answers in a table similar to Table 4.3.7 (template available on the CD), which shows the ratio of bounce height to drop height for the sample data.

Table 4.3.7 Ratios of Bounce Height to Drop Height

Drop Height	Median Tennis Bounce Height	Ratio Tennis Bounce Height to Drop Height	Median Golf Bounce Height	Ratio Golf Bounce Height to Drop Height
30	16	16/30= 0.53	19	19/30 = 0.63
60	33	33/60 = 0.55	38	38/60 = 0.63
90	49	49/90 = 0.54	56	56/90 = 0.62

7. Ask your students to interpret the ratio of the bounce height to the drop height for the tennis ball and golf ball. Note that students' responses should center on a tennis ball bounces back around 54% of the height from which it was dropped. The golf ball bounces back more, somewhere around 63% of the height.

✏ Interpret the Results in the Context of the Original Question

Ask your students to discuss in their groups their answer to the question, "Does the height from which a ball is dropped affect how far it bounces?" Have each group write a summary of the experiment that starts with stating an answer to the question and then supporting their answer by using their analysis. Your students should base their answer on the data collected, key calculations, their scatterplot, and the ratios.

Example of 'Interpret the Results'

Note: The following is not an example of actual student work, but an example of all the parts that should be included in student work.

We think the height from which a ball is dropped does and does not affect the bounce height too much. It depends on what you are looking at. If it's the actual height of the bounce, then it goes up if the drop height goes up. But if it's the ratio of the bounce height to the drop height, then the ratio is constant for a tennis ball or a golf ball—about .54 for the tennis ball and .63 for the golf ball. Our conclusion is based on data we got from dropping a tennis ball three times each from heights of 30, 60, and 90 cm. We dropped the ball three times from each height to get an accurate result. We then took the median of the three data points to represent the bounce height for each drop height. We did the same thing for a golf ball. Here is our scatterplot of median bounce height for each drop height:

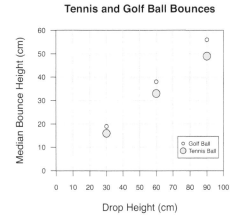

Looking at the scatterplot, we see there is a positive relationship between drop height and bounce height for both tennis and golf balls. We also see that the relationship is pretty linear for both the tennis and the golf ball and that the golf ball bounces higher than the tennis ball at each drop height. The gap between the heights gets wider as the drop gets higher. We now see why our teacher asked us to calculate the ratio of bounce height to drop height. Here are the calculations:

Drop Height	Median Tennis Bounce Height	Ratio Tennis Bounce Height to Drop Height	Median Golf Bounce Height	Ratio Golf Bounce Height to Drop Height
30	16	16/30= 0.53	19	19/30= 0.63
60	33	33/60 = 0.55	38	38/60 = 0.63
90	49	49/90 = 0.54	56	56/90 = 0.62

It's interesting to see that the tennis ball bounces back around 54% of its drop height and the golf ball does better—at around 63%. It's probably because of the composition of a golf ball. We wonder what ratio a "super ball" would have.

Assessment with Answers

A group of students conducted the ball drop experiment using a basketball. Table 4.3.8 contains the results of their experiment when they dropped a basketball from 30, 60, and 90 cm.

Table 4.3.8 Results of Dropping a Basketball

	Basketball		
	30 cm	60 cm	90 cm
Trial 1	22.0	45.0	67.0
Trial 2	23.0	44.0	68.0
Trial 3	22.0	44.0	67.0
Mean	22.3	44.3	67.3
Median	22.0	44.0	67.0
Ratio	0.73	0.73	0.74

1. Find the mean and median bounce height for each drop height and record them in the chart above.

2. Find the ratio of the median bounce height to the median drop height and record them in the chart above.

3. Discuss how the mean and median bounce heights relate to the drop height. Include the ratio of median bounce height to median drop height in your discussion. The height that the basketball bounces is about 73% of the height from which it was dropped.

4. Construct a scatterplot that shows the relationship between the heights from which the basketball was dropped and the median height of the bounce.

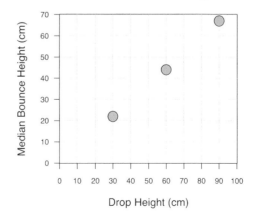

150

5. Describe the graph and the relationship between drop height and median bounce height. The higher the ball is dropped, the higher the bounce.

6. Is the bounce height of a basketball higher than either the tennis ball or golf ball that you used in the investigation? Explain your answer. Based on the sample data given in the investigation, the bounce height of the basketball was higher than both the tennis and golf ball. The median bounce height at the drop heights of 30 cm, 60 cm, and 90 cm were all higher for the basketball than both tennis and golf ball. Based on your class data collected, the answer may differ.

Alternative Assessment

Find a ball at your house and replicate what was done in class with a family member. Drop the ball from 30, 60, and 90 cm. Record your data, find the mean and median, and create a scatterplot. Describe the relationship between drop heights and bounce height and compare your results with the results from the class experiment.

Extensions

1. Ask your students how high they think the ball would bounce if it were dropped from 25 cm? 75 cm? 150 cm? Ask them what they are basing this on? After they make their predictions based on the collected data, have them drop the balls from 25, 75, and 150 cm and compare the results to their predictions. Note that predictions should not be made outside the interval of the original data. However, this should make for an interesting extension, such as seeing if the data trend changes at a certain point.

2. Ask your students how they would carry out this experiment if they wanted to find the ratio of the table tennis ball bounce height to its drop height. Their description should include what drop heights they would use, how many drops from each height, and how they would calculate their answer.

3. Have your students look at their scatterplots. Ask them if it would be possible to imagine a line being drawn to represent the trend in our data? How would drawing this line help us answer the two questions above?

References

Bereska, C., L. C. Bolster, C. A. Bolster, and R. Scheaffer. 1998. *Exploring statistics in the elementary grades: Book one, grades k–6.* White Plains, NY: Dale Seymour.

Franklin, C., G. Kader, D. Mewborn, J. Moreno, R. Peck, M. Perry, and R. Scheaffer. 2007. *Guidelines for assessment and instruction in statistics education (GAISE) report: A pre-k–12 curriculum framework.* Alexandria, VA: American Statistical Association. *www.amstat.org/education/gaise.*

National Council of Teachers of Mathematics. 2000. *Principles and standards for school mathematics.* Reston, VA: National Council of Teachers of Mathematics.

Common Core State Standards for Mathematics. www.corestandards.org.

INVESTIGATION 4.4
CAN YOU ROLL YOUR TONGUE?

Overview

This investigation focuses on students examining an **association** between two **categorical variables**. Specifically, they will investigate whether there is an association between gender and whether a person can roll their tongue. As part of this investigation, students will collect, organize, and analyze data in a **two-way table**; construct and analyze **segmented bar graphs**; and calculate the **percentages** of boys and girls who can roll their tongue. This investigation is based on an activity in *Probability Through Data*, a module in the Data-Driven Mathematics series (1999).

GAISE Components

This investigation follows the four components of statistical problem solving put forth in the *Guidelines for Assessment and Instruction in Statistics Education (GAISE) Report*. The four components are formulate a statistical question that can be answered with data, design and implement a plan to collect appropriate data, analyze the collected data by graphical and numerical methods, and interpret the results of the analysis in the context of the original question. This is a GAISE Level B activity.

Learning Goals

Students will be able to do the following after completing this investigation:

- Organize data collected into a two-way table

- Analyze data in a two-way table

Common Core State Standards for Mathematical Practice

1. Make sense of problems and persevere in solving them.
2. Reason abstractly and quantitatively.
3. Construct viable arguments and critique the reasoning of others.
4. Model with mathematics.

Association

Two categorical variables are associated if certain values of one variable are more likely to occur with certain values of the other variable.

Common Core State Standards
Grade Level Content

6RP3c Find a percent of a quantity as a rate per 100; solve problems involving finding the whole, given a part and the percent.

6SP3 Recognize a statistical question as one that anticipates variability in the data related to the question and accounts for it in the answers.

8.SP.4 Understand that patterns of association also can be seen in bivariate categorical data by displaying frequencies and relative frequencies in a two-way table. Construct and interpret a two-way table summarizing data on two categorical variables collected from the same subjects. Use relative frequencies calculated for rows or columns to describe possible association between the two variables.

Principles and Standards for School Mathematics
Data Analysis and Probability

Grades 6-8 Students should understand and use ratios and percentages to represent quantitative relationships and formulate questions, design studies, and collect data about a characteristic shared by two populations or different characteristics within one population.

Materials

- Data collection sheet (available on the CD)
- Data recording sheet (available on the CD)
- Grid paper
- Color markers

Estimated Time

One day

Instructional Plan

✏ Formulate a Statistical Question

Ask your students to look around their classroom. Pose the question, "Is anyone in the room exactly like you?" "Are identical twins exactly the same?" Discuss that there are many traits or characteristics that make us different from each other. Have students list some of these traits. Examples are hair color, eye color, skin color, blood type, having double-jointed elbows, having "free" earlobes or "attached" earlobes, and whether they can roll their tongue. Discuss with your students that many of these traits are genetic (i.e., inherited or passed on from their parents). Ask which of the traits might have been inherited from their parents.

Tell students there are many traits they could investigate. Indicate that, for this activity, they will be investigating rolling one's tongue (even though it isn't genetic). The statistical question is, "Is gender associated with ability to roll one's tongue?"

✏ Collect Appropriate Data

1. Have one student demonstrate how he/she is able to roll his/her tongue and another demonstrate that he/she is unable to roll his/her tongue.

2. Hand out a data collection sheet to each student. Your students should check whether they are a boy or girl and whether they can roll their tongue. Collect each of the data collection sheets. Figure 4.4.1 is an example of a data collection sheet.

Can't roll tongue

Can roll tongue

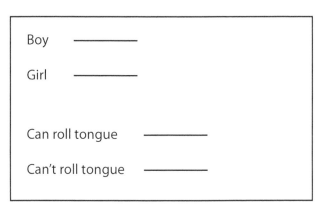

Figure 4.4.1 Data Collection Sheet

3. Hand out a recording sheet (available on the CD) to each student. Take each of the data collection sheets and read whether the sheet is checked boy or girl and whether the student can roll their tongue. As you read each data collection sheet, students should record the data on the recording sheet as shown in Table 4.4.1. Suggest that they write B for boy, G for girl, Y for yes they can roll their tongue, and N for no they cannot roll their tongue.

Table 4.4.1 Example of Class Recording Sheet

Student	Boy or Girl	Roll Your Tongue Yes or No?
1	B	N
2	B	Y
3	G	Y
…	…	…

✏ Analyze the Data

1. Discuss with your students that one way to help analyze the data is to organize the data into a table. Ask them what answers they could record when they were reading the data collection sheets. On the board, display Table 4.4.2. Ask your students to fill in the frequencies (counts) for the four possibilities based on their recording sheet.

Table 4.4.2 Frequency Table

Possibilities	Count/Frequency
Boy – Yes	
Boy – No	
Girl – Yes	
Girl – No	
Total	

2. Explain to your students that their frequency table can be displayed in a different way, called a two-way table. A two-way table organizes data about two categorical variables with rows labeled with the categories of one variable and the columns labeled with the categories of the other variable. In this investigation, the rows of the table are labeled with gender—boys and girls—and the columns are labeled with whether a person can roll their tongue. Demonstrate drawing and labeling the two-way table. The general form is shown in Table 4.4.3. Note that the two-way format is useful when investigating whether there is an association between two categorical variables.

Table 4.4.3 Two-Way Table

	Yes – Can Roll Tongue	No – Can't Roll Tongue	Total
Boy			
Girl			
Total			

3. Label each cell in Table 4.4.3 with letters representing frequencies, as shown in Table 4.4.4.

Table 4.4.4 Example of Completed Two-Way Table

	Yes – Can Roll Tongue	No – Can't Roll Tongue	Total
Boy	a	b	
Girl	c	d	
Total			

4. Explain to your students that the cell labeled "a" will contain the number of students who are both a boy and who said they could roll their tongue. Ask your students what the cell labeled "b" represents. Cell "c"? Cell "d"?

5. Ask your students how many boys are in the sample, using the letters in Table 4.4.4. **Note:** There are "a+b" boys. How many girls? There are "c+d." How many students can roll their tongues? "a+c" can roll their tongues. How many can't? "b+d" can't.

6. Have your students fill in the two-way table based on their class data as recorded in their frequency table, Table 4.4.2. An example of what their table may look like is given in Table 4.4.5.

Table 4.4.5 Row of the Boys' Data from the Two- Way Table

	Yes – Can Roll Tongue	No – Can't Roll Tongue	Total
Boy	8	7	15
Girl	6	4	10
Total	14	11	25

7. Ask your students to use Table 4.4.5 to answer the following questions. As students answer each question, have them point to the appropriate cell.

   a. How many students were in the class?

   b. How many students could roll their tongue?

   c. How many students were girls?

   d. How many students were boys?

   e. How many girls could roll their tongue?

   f. How many boys could roll their tongue?

   g. How many boys could not roll their tongue?

8. Remind your students of the question they are investigating: "Is gender associated with ability to roll one's tongue?" Ask them if they are ready to answer the question. Note that many of your students will say more boys can roll their tongues than girls. Keep asking until someone suggests they should be looking at percentages, not raw counts, as there are more boys than girls in the class.

9. Ask your students to find the percentage of boys who could roll their tongue. To help them answer this question, show them only the row with the boys' data. See Table 4.4.6. Have them find the fraction that answers the question, convert it to a decimal, and then convert it to a percentage. For example, for the boys who can roll their tongue, 8/15 = .53 = 53%.

Table 4.4.6 Row of the Boys' Data from the Two-Way Table

	Yes – Can Roll Tongue	No – Can't Roll Tongue	Total
Boy	8	7	15

10. Using Table 4.4.7, ask your students to find the percentage of girls who can and cannot roll their tongue.

Table 4.4.7 Row of the Girls' Data from the Two-Way Table

	Yes – Can Roll Tongue	No – Can't Roll Tongue	Total
Girl	6	4	10

11. Ask your students to put their percentages in a two-way table. See Table 4.4.8. Note that the Total row percentages are each 100%.

Table 4.4.8 Example of Row Percentages

	Yes – Can Roll Tongue	No – Can't Roll Tongue	Total
Boy	8/15 = .53 = 53%	7/15 = .47 = 47%	15/15 = 1.00 = 100%
Girl	6/10 = .60 = 60%	4/10 = .40 = 40%	10/10 = 1.00 = 100%
Total			

12. To help your students visualize the different percentages of boys and girls who can and cannot roll their tongue, demonstrate the construction of a segmented bar graph. Using Table 4.4.8, a segmented bar graph is shown in Figure 4.4.2. Note that the percentages could also be visualized in side-by-side bar graphs.

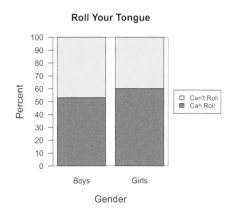
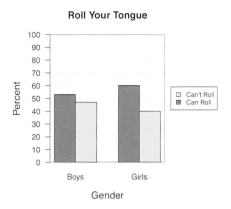

Figure 4.4.2 Segmented bar graph and side-by-side bar graph of example class data

✐ Interpret the Results in the Context of the Original Question

1. Have your students recall the original statistical question, "Is gender associated with ability to roll one's tongue?" Have each group of students write an answer to the question and then justify it using the two-way table, appropriate calculations involving percentages, and the segmented bar graph. Suggest to your students that they should focus on the difference in the percentages and the heights of the bars in the segmented bar graph. Remind your students that an association exists between two categorical variables if knowing the response of one of the variables helps to know what the response might be of the other variable. Does knowing a girl was chosen from the group help know whether she can roll her tongue? Similarly, does knowing a boy was chosen help know whether he has the ability to roll his tongue? Have each group of students present their results to the class.

Example of 'Interpret the Results' ✐

Note: The following is not an example of actual student work, but an example of all the parts that should be included in student work.

In our biology class, we often talk about genetics, so we thought a good statistics project in our mathematics class would be to take a genetic trait and see if it is associated with gender. We chose rolling our tongues. (After our study was complete, we found out that rolling one's tongue is not actually genetic. It is a learned trait. But it was fun doing the experiment anyway.) Our statistical question was "Is gender associated with ability to roll one's tongue?" We collected data by making a list of boys or girls and whether they could roll their tongue. We then counted how many there were in each of the four categories and organized the data in a two-way table like this one.

	Yes – Can Roll Tongue	No – Can't Roll Tongue	Total
Boy	8	7	15
Girl	6	4	10
Total	14	11	25

So, to answer the question, some of us say boys are more likely to roll their tongues than girls are. But, we messed up because there were more boys in class than girls. So, we should be looking at percentages, not counts. When we calculated the percentages, we almost based them on 25, but realized they had to be calculated within boys' and girls' totals. So, here is our table of row percentages.

	Yes – Can Roll Tongue	No – Can't Roll Tongue	Total
Boy	8/15 = .53 = 53%	7/15 = .47 = 47%	15/15 = 1.00 = 100%
Girl	6/10 = .60 = 60%	4/10 = .40 = 40%	10/10 = 1.00 = 100%
Total			

The actual answer to our question is that a higher percentage of girls can roll their tongues as compared to boys. Sixty percent of girls could roll their tongues compared to 53% of boys. Our teacher showed us how to visualize these results in what is called a segmented bar graph. It makes it clear that the percentage of girls is higher.

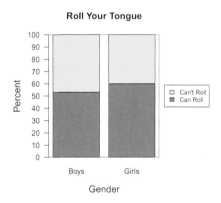

But we debated whether gender and ability to roll one's tongue are associated because some of us thought that 53% and 60% are kind of close and so the variables are not associated. Others thought the percentages were far enough apart to claim the variables are associated. Our teacher said we will learn more about association in high school.

Assessment with Answers

A survey asked a group of students if they participated in a sport and if they played a musical instrument. Table 4.4.7 shows the survey results.

Table 4.4.7 Survey Results

	Music Yes	Music No	Total
Sport Yes	18	2	20
Sport No	8	22	30
Total	26	24	50

Use the table to answer the following questions:

1. How many students said they participated in a sport? Twenty said they participated in a sport.

2. How many students said they did not play a musical instrument? Twenty-four said they did not play a musical instrument.

3. What does the number 8 represent in the table? The number 8 represents the number of students who said no to sports and yes to music.

4. What percentage of those who said they participated in a sport also played a musical instrument? 18/20 = .90.

5. What percentage of those who said they did not participate in a sport played a musical instrument? 8/30 = .27.

6. If a student participates in a sport, are they more likely to play a musical instrument than a student who does not participate in a sport? Use words, numbers, and graphs to explain your answer.

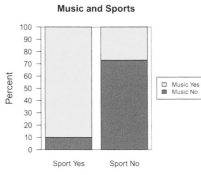

Students who do not participate in a sport are much less likely to play a musical instrument than those who do participate in a sport. Twenty-seven percent of students who do not participate in a sport also played an instrument while 90%

of those that did participate in a sport played an instrument. The segmented bar graph shows the big difference between the groups who do and don't play sports and whether they play an instrument. We can say that participation in sports and playing a musical instrument are associated.

Extensions

1. Ask students to collect data at home. Each student should ask one parent/guardian if he/she could roll his/her tongue. Collect data in a table during the next class period:

Possibilities	Number
Student yes – Parent/guardian yes	
Student yes – Parent/guardian no	
Student no – Parent/guardian yes	
Student no – Parent/guardian no	

Your students should organize the data in a two-way table. Based on the table and calculated percents, students should determine if there appears to be an association between whether the parent/guardian can roll his/her tongue and whether the student can roll his/her tongue.

2. Your students could investigate if there appears to be an association between whether a person is left-handed or right-handed and whether they are left-thumbed or right-thumbed. **Note:** To determine whether one is left- or right-thumbed, have your students clasp their hands together immediately without thinking about it. Then look at the pictures to the left to determine the category. Students could collect class data and analyze the data to determine if there appears to be an association.

Right-thumbed

Left-thumbed

References

Franklin, C., G. Kader, D. Mewborn, J. Moreno, R. Peck, M. Perry, and R. Scheaffer. 2007. *Guidelines for assessment and instruction in statistics education (GAISE) report: A pre-k–12 curriculum framework.* Alexandria, VA: American Statistical Association. *www.amstat.org/education/gaise.*

Hopfensperger, P., H. Kranendonk, and R. Scheaffer. 1999. *Probability through data.* New York, NY: Dale Seymour.

National Council of Teachers of Mathematics. 2000. *Principles and standards for school mathematics.* Reston, VA: National Council of Teachers of Mathematics.

Common Core State Standards for Mathematics, www.corestandards.org.

EXPLORING RELATIONSHIP

INVESTIGATION 5.1
DO NAMES AND COST RELATE?

Overview

In Investigation 3.3, "How Expensive Is Your Name?" students analyzed the statistical question, "How expensive is it to monogram their first names onto a T-shirt?" Instead of using a constant cost per letter, as was done there, the cost of a letter is based on its frequency of use in the English language in this investigation. Students will investigate the concept of any positive and negative **relationship** between two **quantitative** variables by constructing **scatterplots** of length of first name and cost of first name, as well as cost of first and last names.

GAISE Components

This investigation follows the four components of statistical problem solving put forth in the *Guidelines for Assessment and Instruction in Statistics Education (GAISE) Report.* The four components are formulate a statistical question that can be answered with data, design and implement a plan to collect appropriate data, analyze the collected data by graphical and numerical methods, and interpret the results of the analysis in the context of the original question. This is a GAISE Level B activity.

Learning Goals

Students will be able to do the following after completing this investigation:

- Graph ordered pairs on a scatterplot
- Interpret data presented in a scatterplot

Common Core State Standards for Mathematical Practice

1. Make sense of problems and persevere in solving them.
2. Reason abstractly and quantitatively.
3. Construct viable arguments and critique the reasoning of others.
4. Model with mathematics.

Common Core State Standards Grade Level Content

8.SP.1 Construct and interpret scatter plots for bivariate measurement data to investigate patterns of association between two quantities.

NCTM Principles and Standards for School Mathematics

Algebra

Grades 3–5 All students should represent and analyze patterns and functions, using words, tables and graphs; model problem situations with objects and use representations such as graphs, tables, and equations to draw conclusions.

Grades 6–8 All students should relate and compare different forms of representation for a relationship.

Data Analysis and Probability

Grades 3–5 All students should propose and justify conclusions and predictions that are based on data; represent data using tables and graphs.

Grades 6–8 All students should make conjectures about possible relationships between two characteristics of a sample based on scatterplots of the data.

Materials

- Table 5.1.1 Occurrence of Letter Percentages (available on the CD)
- Table 5.1.2 Cost of Letters (available on the CD)
- Data collection sheet (available on the CD)
- Small sticky notes (two for each student)
- Enough board space for two large graphs

Estimated Time

1–2 days

Instructional Plan

✏ Formulate a Statistical Question

1. Before creating a statistical question to investigate, spend some time having your students understand how costs could be assigned to letters based on the frequency of occurrence of letters in the English language. Ask your students which letter of our alphabet they believe is used most often. Encourage them to activate their prior knowledge by asking them to think about playing or watching games such as Scrabble, Hangman, and Wheel of Fortune. You may have them count the letters in a page of their textbook

and create a frequency/percentage table. This investigation will use the letter percentages as shown in Table 5.1.1, which is from Wikipedia.

Table 5.1.1 Occurrence of Letter Percentages

Letter	a	b	c	d	e	f	g	h	i
Percentage	8.2%	1.4%	2.8%	4.2%	12.7%	2.2%	2.0%	6.1%	7.0%
Letter	j	k	l	m	n	o	p	q	r
Percentage	0.2%	0.8%	4.0%	2.4%	6.7%	7.5%	1.9%	0.1%	6.0%
Letter	s	t	u	v	w	x	y	z	
Percentage	6.3%	9.1%	2.7%	1.0%	2.4%	0.2%	2.0%	0.1%	

2. Have your students make some observations about the table. For example, what must be the sum of all of the percentages in the table? Why? Which letter occurs most often? Least often? Do vowels occur more often than consonants? Be sure your students understand that letters with high percentages occur more frequently and letters with low percentages occur less frequently.

3. Display Table 5.1.2 Cost of Letters. Have your students make some observations about this table. For example, which letters are the most expensive? Least expensive? How is Table 5.1.2 Cost of Letters related to Table 5.1.1 Occurrence of Letter Percentages? Note that your students should discover that the letters occurring more frequently were assigned higher monetary costs, and the letters occurring less frequently were assigned lower monetary costs. Ask your students if other assignments of costs to letters could have been made. Ask your students what the cost of names with many vowels in them might be as compared to those with few vowels.

Table 5.1.2 Cost of Letters (cents)

A	B	C	D	E	F	G	H	I	J	K	L	M
6¢	3¢	3¢	4¢	7¢	3¢	3¢	5¢	5¢	1¢	2¢	4¢	3¢
N	O	P	Q	R	S	T	U	V	W	X	Y	Z
5¢	5¢	3¢	1¢	5¢	5¢	6¢	3¢	3¢	1¢	3¢	1¢	

4. Ask your students if they think there is a relationship between the length of their first name and the cost of their first name. More specifically, have them discuss which names would be the most expensive—names with more vowels or names with more overall letters? Do they think a person who has a long first name will have an expensive first name? In addition, have them consider the comparative cost of their first and last names. Do they think a person who has an expensive first name will have an expensive last name, or perhaps an inexpensive last name? Explain that they will be looking for these kinds of relationships. Lead your students to formulate the statistical questions, "Is there a relationship between the length of first names and the cost of first names?" and "Is there a relationship between the cost of first and last names?"

✏ Collect Appropriate Data

1. Before collecting data, for consistency purposes, decide whether all students will use their given name or a nickname (e.g., Jennifer or Jenny; Katherine or Katie, Joseph or JP).

2. Using Table 5.1.2, ask each of your students to find the lengths and costs of their own first and last names. For example, John Smith would have a length of 4 for his first name, a cost of 16¢ for his first name, a length of 5 for his last name, and a cost of 24¢ for his last name.

3. Collect the class data on the data collection sheet as in Table 5.1.3.

Table 5.1.3 Data Collection Sheet 💿

Student	Length of First Name	Cost of First Name (¢)	Length of Last Name	Cost of Last Name (¢)
1				
2				
3				
4				
5				
...				

4. For this investigation, the data in Table 5.1.4 that were collected from an 8th-grade class of 18 students will be used as an example.

Table 5.1.4 Sample Data of Costs of First and Last Names

Student	Length of First Name	Cost of First Name (¢)	Length of Last Name	Cost of Last Name (¢)
1	5	26	11	43
2	4	17	7	38
3	5	20	8	42
4	8	39	8	42
5	6	25	6	35
6	8	41	7	38
7	4	20	7	33
8	7	34	6	30
9	4	17	6	29
10	5	27	9	45
11	5	26	10	46
12	9	48	5	20
13	7	32	5	21
14	5	26	8	40
15	7	36	5	24
16	5	28	6	24
17	7	39	7	31
18	7	32	8	29

✏ **Analyze the Data**

1. Ask your students to look at the columns Length of First Name and Cost of First Name. Tell them that they are to determine if there is a relationship between the length of the first name and its cost to monogram. Explain that a positive relationship means points on the graph go from the lower left part to the upper right part, so shorter names would be less expensive and longer names would be more expensive.

2. Explain to your students that constructing a scatterplot may help them discover any relationship between length of first name and its cost. Discuss with them how to construct a scatterplot. On the board, draw a horizontal axis labeled Length of First Name and a vertical axis labeled Cost of First Name. Discuss with your students the scales needed on both axes.

3. Give each student a small sticky note. On the sticky note, your students should write length and cost of their first name as an ordered pair. Figure 5.1.1 shows what John Smith would write on his sticky note.

168

Figure 5.1.1 Sticky note with length of first name and cost of first name written as an ordered pair

4. Have your students place their sticky notes at the appropriate coordinate location on the scatterplot. Figure 5.1.2 is a scatterplot based on the 8th-grade class data. **Note:** This sample graph is drawn with points, while your class graph will have sticky notes.

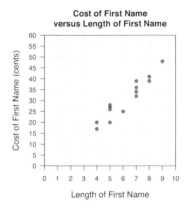

Figure 5.1.2 Scatterplot of cost (¢) of first name versus length of first name. **Note:** There are two data points at coordinate (4,17), three at (5,26), and two at (7,32).

5. Point to one of the student's sticky notes and ask your students what the coordinates of that point represent.

6. Ask your students whether they observe a pattern or relationship between the length of first name and the cost of first name. Explain that the scatterplot shows a positive trend or relationship between the length of first name and its cost. The points are generally going from the lower left part of the graph to the upper right part of the graph. Explain that this means a person who has a long first name would tend to have a more costly first name, and a person who has a short first name would tend to have a less costly first name.

7. Ask your students why they think this graph shows a positive relationship.

8. Refer to the data collection sheet (Table 5.1.4). Ask your students to look at the columns Cost of First Name and Cost of Last Name. Ask them if they see any relationship between these two variables.

9. Give students another sticky note and ask them to record the cost of their first name and the cost of their last name as an ordered pair. Figure 5.1.3 shows what John Smith would write on his sticky note.

Figure 5.1.3 Sticky note of cost of first and cost of last name for John Smith written as an ordered pair

10. On the board, draw a horizontal axis labeled Cost of First Name and a vertical axis labeled Cost of Last Name. Discuss with your students the scales needed on both axes.

11. Have your students place their sticky notes at the appropriate coordinate locations on the scatterplot. Figure 5.1.4 is a scatterplot based on the 8th-grade class data. Note: This sample graph is drawn with points, while your class graph will have sticky notes.

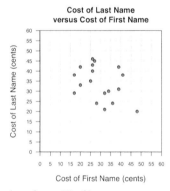

Figure 5.1.4 Scatterplot of cost (¢) of last name versus cost (¢) of first name

12. Ask your students if they observe any pattern or relationship between the cost of monogramming first names and the cost of monogramming last names. Explain to your students that the scatterplot shows a negative trend or relationship between the cost of the first and last names. The points are generally going from the upper left part of the graph to the lower right part of the graph. Explain that this means a higher cost of the first name is related with a lower cost of the last name, or a person who has an expensive first name would tend to have a less expensive last name.

13. Ask your students why they think the cost of monogramming one's first name has a negative relationship with the cost of monogramming one's last name.

✏ Interpret the Results in the Context of the Original Question

1. Remind your students of the original questions they have been investigating: "Is there a relationship between the length of first names and the cost of first names?" and "Is there a relationship between the cost of first name and cost of last name?" Have them write a summary of their investigation by answering the questions and using their graphical analysis to support their answers.

2. Ask your students if they think the cost of names using Table 5.1.2 in this investigation would be the same as for students in England? France? China? **Note:** the name John translates to Juan in Spanish and Yue Han in Chinese.

Example of 'Interpret the Results' 💿

Note: The following is not an example of actual student work, but an example of all the parts that should be included in student work.

In this investigation, we looked at two questions. One was on relating the length of our first names and the cost of monogramming them on T-shirts. The second question was on investigating if the cost of monogramming our first names and last names were related. The assignment of costs to letters was based on the frequency of usage of letters in English. High-frequency letters cost more and low-frequency letters cost less. In Scrabble, it's the opposite, with the letters that don't occur very often being worth more. To see how the length of our first name and its cost are related, we displayed the length and cost of our first names on a scatterplot using sticky notes. We did the same for the cost of our first and last names. Here were our graphs.

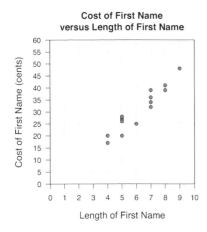

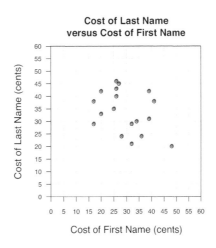

We saw that the cost of the name was higher for longer names, which meant there was a positive association between the length of our first name and its cost. We also investigated the relationship between the cost of our first and cost of our last name. We displayed a scatterplot of the cost of both names and observed that the higher costs of the first names were associated with lower costs of the last names. This meant there was a negative relationship between the cost of the first and last names.

We are going to continue this study by analyzing names in foreign countries such as China and Russia. For example, John in Chinese is Yue Han, which has a cost of 29 cents. John in English was 16 cents. Maybe Chinese names have more vowels, so they might cost more. We'll see.

Assessment with Answers

A group of 8th-grade students investigated the statistical question, "Is there a relationship between the length of their last name and the cost of their last name." Figure 5.1.5 is a scatterplot of the length of the students' last names and the cost of their last names.

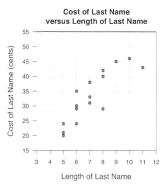

Figure 5.1.5 Scatterplot of cost (¢) of last name versus length of last name

1. Choose a point on the graph and describe what it means in the context of the variables. The point (10,46) means a last name of 10 letters would cost 46¢.

2. If a student has a long last name, does that student tend to have a more or less expensive cost for their last name? Explain your answer. A student with a long last name would tend to have a more expensive last name.

3. Overall, is there a relationship between the length of a student's last name and the cost of their last name? Use words and numbers to explain your answer. There is a positive relationship between length of last name and cost. As the length of the name increases, the cost tends to increase.

172

Alternative Assessment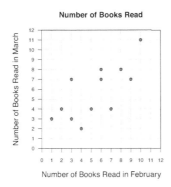
with Answers

March is National Reading Month and a teacher wanted to know if her students read more books in March than in February. Figure 5.1.6 is a scatterplot of the number of books sixth-graders each read during February and March.

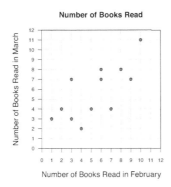

Number of Books Read

Figure 5.1.6 Scatterplot of number of books read by sixth-graders in March versus number of books read by sixth-graders in February

1. Choose a point and describe what it means in the context of the variables. Point (10,11) means this student read 10 books in February and 11 books in March.

2. If a student read many books in February, what did that student tend to do in March? Explain your answer. The student read many books in March as well.

3. Overall, is there a relationship between the number of books sixth-graders read in February and the number of books they read in March? Use words and/or numbers to explain your answer. Yes, the trend in the graph shows that the more books read in February, the more books read in March. The graph goes from the lower left to the upper right.

Extension

1. Have your students investigate the possibility of a relationship between the total length of both names and the total cost of both names.

2. The relevance of this investigation involving the frequency of letters is in the discipline of cryptography. You may want to discuss the deciphering of secret codes with your students.

References

Franklin, C., G. Kader, D. Mewborn, J. Moreno, R. Peck, M. Perry, and R. Scheaffer. 2007. *Guidelines for assessment and instruction in statistics education (GAISE) report: A pre-k–12 curriculum framework*. Alexandria, VA: American Statistical Association. *www.amstat.org/education/gaise*.

National Council of Teachers of Mathematics. 2000. *Principles and standards for school mathematics*. Reston, VA: National Council of Teachers of Mathematics.

Common Core State Standards for Mathematics, *www.corestandards.org*.

Wikipedia, *http://en.wikipedia.org/wiki/Letter_frequency*.

Investigation 5.2
How Tall Were the Ancestors of Laetoli?

Overview

The focus of this investigation is to look for and measure the degree of any **relationship** between two **quantitative** variables, specifically height and foot length. The motivation for this study comes from a science dig. Footprints were found that were determined to be more than 3 million years old. It is of interest to predict how tall those ancestors might have been based on the lengths of their footprints. Students will investigate whether there is a relationship between their own height and foot length. They will collect, organize, and analyze such data and then informally predict what the height of the ancestors might have been.

GAISE Components

This investigation follows the four components of statistical problem solving put forth in the *Guidelines for Assessment and Instruction in Statistics Education (GAISE) Report*. The four components are formulate a statistical question that can be answered with data, design and implement a plan to collect appropriate data, analyze the collected data by graphical and numerical methods, and interpret the results of the analysis in the context of the original question. This is a GAISE Level B activity.

Learning Goals

Students will be able to do the following after completing this investigation:

- Learn to make conjectures about the relationship between two quantitative variables

- Demonstrate an ability to organize their data and display them in a scatterplot

- Learn to quantify the degree of relationship between two quantitative variables by developing the Quadrant Count Ratio (QCR)

Common Core State Standards for Mathematical Practice

1. Make sense of problems and persevere in solving them.
2. Reason abstractly and quantitatively.
3. Construct viable arguments and critique the reasoning of others.
4. Model with mathematics.
6. Attend to precision.

Common Core State Standard Grade level Content

8.SP.1 Construct and interpret scatterplots for bivariate measurement data to investigate patterns of association between two quantities. Describe patterns such as clustering, outliers, positive or negative association, linear association, and nonlinear association.

NCTM Principles and Standards for School Mathematics

Data Analysis and Probability

Grades 6-8 Students should formulate questions, design studies, and collect data about a characteristic shared by two populations or different characteristics within one population; select, create, and use appropriate graphical representations of data, including histograms, boxplots, and scatterplots.

Materials

- Class data recording sheet (available on the CD)
- Sticker dots (3/4" diameter, four colors - green, blue, yellow, and red)
- Metric sticks
- Tape
- Graph paper
- Calculators
- Laetoli background information (available on the CD)

Estimated Time

Two days

Instructional Plan

✏️ **Formulate a Statistical Question**

1. Begin this investigation by asking your students if they think there is any relationship between the size of a person's foot and his/her height. Do people with longer feet tend to be taller? Explain to your students that scientists look for relationships like this so they can estimate the height of people who lived a long time ago. Share with your students the following background information from Wikipedia about Laetoli, Tanzania (available on the CD).

There is a place in Tanzania, Africa, known as Laetoli. It is a special place because it is where scientists believe our ancestors of long ago walked side-by-side. It is where scientists have worked to get an understanding of the past.

In the late 1970s, two sets of footprints were discovered at Laetoli. There were 70 footprints in two side-by-side lines 30 meters long, preserved in volcanic ash. Apparently, a volcano exploded sending ash everywhere and the two individuals just happened to walk through the area, preserving their footprints. Fossil remains in the area tell scientists that the ancestors who left the footprints found at Laetoli lived about 3.5 million years ago.

We know the size of the feet because Dr. Mary Leakey, an anthropologist, and her team made copies of the prints using plaster casts. The locations of the footprints were put on a map, so the length of stride (distance between footprints) also can be determined. Based on these observations, foot dimensions and stride length for the two ancestors are given in Table 5.2.1. These are averages based on the 70 observed footprints.

Table 5.2.1 Footprint Data Collected by Dr. Leakey at Laetoli

	Ancestor 1	Ancestor 2
Length of Footprint	21.5 cm	18.5 cm
Width of Footprint	10 cm	8.8 cm
Length of Stride	47.2 cm	28.7

Much has been learned from these footprints. They share many characteristics with the prints made by modern human feet.

A research question of interest to the scientists was "How tall were these ancestors at Laetoli?" The foot length, foot width, and length of stride can be used to produce estimates of the heights of these ancestors.

2. After explaining the background information, discuss with your students how they can help the scientists answer the question, "How tall were these ancestors at Laetoli?" Tell your students they are going to focus on whether foot length and height are related. **Note:** Depending on the sensitivity of measuring feet, you may have your students measure shoe length instead. (However, to be realistic, the ancestors did not wear anything on their feet.) Although collecting real data is desirable, there is a sample set of class data given in Table 5.2.2.

3. Lead your students to formulate the statistical question, "What, if any, is the relationship between height and foot size of humans?"

✏ Collect Appropriate Data

1. Discuss with your students how they are to measure the length of their right foot. The measurements should be made in centimeters and without shoes from the back of the foot to the longest forward point of their toes. **Note:** You may want to have your students press the back of their right foot against a wall to increase the accuracy of the measurement. When measuring the height of the person, remind students they should stand straight with their back against a wall.

2. After students have measured the length of both their right foot and their height, collect the class data on the recording form (available on the CD). Table 5.2.2 is a sample set of data collected from a class of 8th-graders.

Table 5.2.2 Sample Set of 8th-Grade Class Data

Student Number	Foot Length cm	Height cm	Student Number	Foot Length cm	Height cm
1	28	175	14	24	168
2	26	181	15	23	168
3	24	168	16	23	176
4	26	168	17	27	177
5	27	178	18	25	171
6	24	174	19	22	160
7	28	179	20	27	187
8	23	157	21	28	167
9	29	190	22	27	184
10	26	170	23	29	181
11	23	169	24	27	174
12	23	166	25	22	155
13	26	174	26	24	170

✏ **Analyze the Data**

1. Ask your students to find the mean length of the right foot data and the mean of the height data.

2. Draw a large scatterplot on the board and plot the ordered pair (mean foot length, mean height) with a black dot. For the sample class data, the point is (25.4, 172.6).

3. Ask all students with above-average right foot length and above-average height to stand. Give them a green "sticker dot" and have them place their stickers on the graph at the appropriate coordinates.

4. Ask all students with below-average right foot length and above-average height to stand. Give them a blue "sticker dot" and have them place their stickers on the graph at the appropriate coordinates.

5. Ask all students with below-average right foot length and below-average height to stand. Give them an orange "sticker dot" and have them place their stickers on the graph at the appropriate coordinates.

6. Ask all students with above-average right foot length and below-average height to stand. Give them a red "sticker dot" and have them place their stickers on the graph at the appropriate coordinates. Figure 5.2.1 is a scatterplot of the sample set of data collected from an 8th-grade class. Note the ordered pair of means is the black dot in the scatterplot.

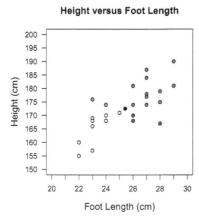

Height versus Foot Length

Figure 5.2.1 Class scatterplot of height versus foot length. **Note:** There is a duplicate data point at (24, 168).

7. Ask your students what trends they observe in the graph. Note that they should say there is a positive trend with longer foot lengths related to taller heights and shorter foot lengths related to shorter heights. Discuss

with your students that, in statistics, single summary numbers are calculated for a data set that tell us something about the data set. For example, when asked to characterize a central tendency for a data set, three summary statistics have been developed: the mode (most often), median (middle of the ordered data), and mean (a fair share value or balance point). Each is a single number. Similarly, when characterizing the spread of a data set, three summary statistics have been developed: the range (overall span of the data), interquartile range (span of the middle 50% of the data), and mean absolute deviation (MAD, a fair share value for how far the data are in terms of absolute distance from their mean). In this investigation of two variables, we want to develop a summary statistic (single number) that measures how related two quantitative variables are to each other. The following steps help your students develop such a summary statistic.

8. Draw a vertical line through the center point (black dot) extended to the x-axis; indicate the mean of X, 25.4 cm, on the x-axis. Similarly, draw a horizontal line through the center point (black dot) extended to the y-axis; indicate the mean of Y, 172.6 cm, on the y-axis.

9. Point to different colored dots and ask your students to explain what the dots represent in relation to the center point, given by the coordinate pair (the mean foot length, the mean height).

10. Number the four quadrants as shown in Figure 5.2.2.

    Quadrant I: Green dots

    Quadrant II: Blue dots

    Quadrant III: Orange dots

    Quadrant IV: Red dots

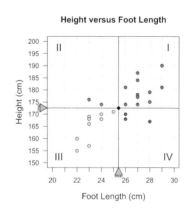

Figure 5.2.2 Scatterplot of height versus foot length showing the quadrants

180

11. Ask your students where most of the stickers are. Determine the number of dots in each quadrant and put the number on the graph in the respective quadrants. Figure 5.2.3 shows the sample class data with the number of ordered pairs written in each quadrant. Note that there are two data points at (24,168) so there are 10 data points in quadrant III.

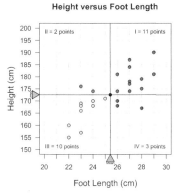

Figure 5.2.3 Scatterplot showing number of ordered pairs in each quadrant

12. Ask your students what a dot in Quadrant I represents. (People with above average foot length and above-average height). Ask what a dot in Quadrant III represents. (People with below-average foot length and below-average height)

13. Explain to your students that this graph indicates a **positive relationship** between the variables foot length and height. Generally, two numeric variables are **positively related** when above-average values of one variable tend to occur with above-average values of the other and when below-average values of one variable tend to occur with below-average values of the other. **Negative relationship** between two variables occurs when below-average values of one variable tend to occur with above-average values of the other and when above-average values of one variable tend to occur with below-average values of the other.

14. Explain to your students that we would like to have a single number that helps describe the degree of relationship seen in the graph. A **correlation coefficient** is a number that measures the direction and strength of a relationship between two variables. One such correlation coefficient is called the **Quadrant Count Ratio** (QCR). The QCR is defined as:

$$QCR = \frac{\text{(Number of Data Points in Quadrants I and III)} - \text{(Number of Data Points in Quadrants II and IV)}}{\text{Total Number of Points}}$$

15. Have your students find the QCR for the class data. For the example:

$$QCR = \frac{((11 + 10) - (2 + 3))}{26} = \frac{(21 - 5)}{26} = \frac{16}{26} = 0.62$$

16. Ask your students to find the value of the QCR if all the ordered pairs are located in quadrants I and III. Ask your students if it is possible to get a QCR greater than 1 (such as 1.5). Ask your students to find the value of the QCR if all the ordered pairs are located in quadrants II and IV. Ask your students if it is possible to get a QCR less than -1 (such as -1.9).

17. Explain to your students that the closer the value is to +1, the stronger the positive relationship is. The closer to -1 suggests a stronger negative relationship. Close to 0 would indicate no relationship. Have them look at the scatterplot and explain why that should be.

18. Indicate on a number line where the class value of QCR is and ask students what the value indicates about the strength of the relationship between height and foot length. Figure 5.2.4 shows the location of the QCR for the sample set of data.

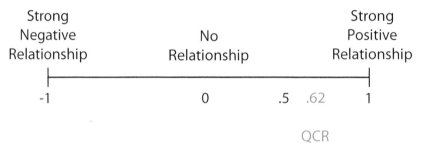

Figure 5.2.4 Strength of relationship on a number line

19. Ask your students to look at Figure 5.2.3 and, assuming the relationship of height to foot length is the same for the ancestors of Laetoli as it is in this data set, what color of sticker would the ancestors have based on a mean footprint of 21.5 cm? Note that they should say orange and that the ancestors had shorter feet than their own and were shorter in height than their own average height.

✏ Interpret the Results in the Context of the Original Question

1. Have your students recall the original statistical question, "What, if any, is the relationship between height and foot size of humans?" Have your students write a brief report that answers the question and justifies their answer by using the analysis they did in class. In addition, remind your students that what prompted the statistical question involving height and foot length was an interest in trying to estimate the heights of the two ancestors from Laetoli, as we know only the length of their footprints. Have your students include in their report how they might go about coming up with an estimate of the height of the Laetoli ancestors. Indicate that you are not as interested in their actual estimate as you are in the process they are suggesting for determining the estimate. (See the extension for further development.)

2. Ask your students how they think the relationship between height and foot length would change from what they found using their class data if they collected data on height and foot length from all the teachers in the school.

Example of 'Interpret the Results' 💿

Note: The following is not an example of actual student work, but an example of all the parts that should be included in student work.

For a statistics project, we got an idea from an anthropological study by Dr. Leakey, who found footprints of 3.6 million–old ancestors in Laetoli, Tanzania. The study had the ancestors footprint lengths, and we were wondering how tall they might have been. One of the set of footprints had a mean footprint of 21.5 cm. Our statistical question was, "Is there a relationship between human height and foot length?" Our data were the lengths of our right foot and our height. There were 26 paired data points in our class.

The first thing we did was to draw a picture, a scatterplot, with height on the vertical axis and foot length on the horizontal axis. It looked like people with longer feet were taller and those with shorter feet were shorter. To see that, we gave out sticker dots and placed them on a big scatterplot on the board. The dots were determined by whether our height was above or below the mean height of 172.6 cm and how our foot length compared to the mean 25.4 cm. Green dots were for (above 25.4 foot length, above 172.6 height); blue for (below, above); orange for (below, below); and red for (above, below). We added vertical and horizontal lines through the paired mean point. The scatterplot looked like this:

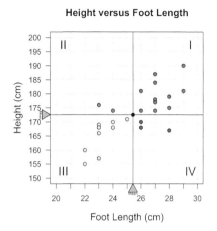

Height versus Foot Length

We could see a definite trend from the lower left to the upper right. In statistics, single numbers called summary statistics are often calculated to indicate the degree of some characteristic. So, our teacher suggested we count the number of points in the first and third quadrants and subtract the numbers in quadrants two and four, and then take the mean and call the result the Quadrant Count Ratio (QCR). For our data, QCR = ((11+10) − (2+3))/26 = 0.62. If all the data had been in quadrants one and three, the QCR would have been 1. So, we decided that .62 was pretty good and that it reflected a positive relationship. We then decided that our Laetoli ancestors would have had orange stickers, since the mean footprint we had for them was 21.5 and, from our scatterplot, there was no way the sticker could be blue. We were thinking about doing this study on all our teachers to get a new data set and see if it differs from ours. There's a difference of opinion. Some of us think it would have more variation because the ages of the teachers are more spread out than our ages.

Assessment with Answers

A group of students measured their height and arm span in centimeters. Table 5.2.3 shows the data they collected, and the scatterplot of the data is shown in Figure 5.2.5.

Table 5.2.3 Height and Arm Span (cm)

Height	Arm Span	Height	Arm Span
155	151	173	170
162	162	175	166
162	161	176	171
163	172	176	173
164	167	178	173
164	155	178	166
165	163	181	183
165	165	183	181
166	167	183	178
166	164	183	174
168	165	183	180
171	164	185	177
171	168	188	185

Arm Span versus Height

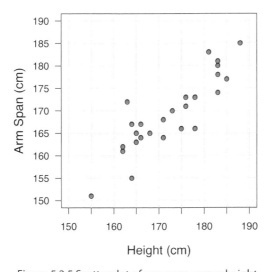

Figure 5.2.5 Scatterplot of arm span versus height

1. **Describe the relationship between arm span and height.** There is a positive relationship between arm span and height. Higher values of arm span tend to occur with higher values in height; lower values of arm span tend to occur with lower values in height.

2. **Find the mean height and the mean arm span.** Mean height = 172.5 cm and the mean arm span = 169.3.

3. Locate the point (mean height, mean arm span) on the graph and draw a horizontal line and a vertical line through the point.

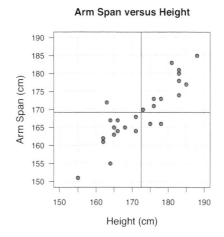

Arm Span versus Height

Figure 5.2.6 Scatterplot showing means and vertical and horizontal lines

4. Find the value of the QCR. QCR = ((11 + 12) - (1 + 2))/26 = (23 - 3)/26 = 20/26 = .77

5. Interpret the value of the QCR. Fairly strong positive relationship between height and arm span. This indicates that height is a pretty good predictor for arm span.

Extension

To determine an estimate for the height of the Laetoli ancestors, suggest the following:

1. Consider the scatterplot of height versus foot length as shown in Figure 5.2.7. Hand out a copy of this scatterplot to your students.

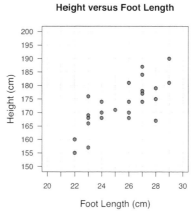

Height versus Foot Length

Figure 5.2.7 Scatterplot of height versus foot length. **Note:** There is a duplicate data point at (24,168).

2. Demonstrate and discuss an eyeball line on the class scatterplot using a piece of string or yarn. Ask your students what property the line should have. Lead them to suggesting that the line should "fit" the data fairly well.

3. Draw the line on the class graph and demonstrate making a prediction using the line. For a given value of X—for example, 21.5 for Laetoli ancestor 1—from 21.5 on the X axis, move vertically up to the line, then horizontally to the y-axis, as shown in Figure 5.2.8.

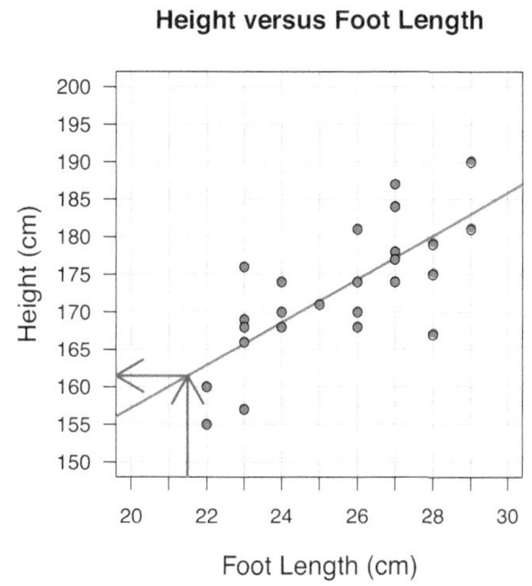

Height versus Foot Length

Figure 5.2.8 Scatterplot of height versus foot length with eyeball fit line. **Note:** There is a duplicate data point at (24,168).

4. Have each student draw their eyeball fit line and use the line to make a prediction for the two Laetoli ancestors.

References

Franklin, C., G. Kader, D. Mewborn, J. Moreno, R. Peck, M. Perry, and R. Scheaffer. 2007. *Guidelines for assessment and instruction in statistics education (GAISE) report: A pre-k–12 curriculum framework.* Alexandria, VA: American Statistical Association. *www.amstat.org/education/gaise.*

National Council of Teachers of Mathematics. 2000. *Principles and standards for school mathematics.* Reston, VA: National Council of Teachers of Mathematics.

Common Core State Standards for Mathematics, www.corestandards.org.

Laetoli, *http://en.wikipedia.org/wiki/Laetoli.*

INVESTIGATION 5.3
HOW LONG DOES IT TAKE TO PERFORM THE WAVE?

Overview

The focus of this investigation is looking for a **relationship** between two **quantitative** variables. Specifically, students will investigate whether there is a relationship between number of people and how long it takes them to perform the "wave." As part of this investigation, students will collect, organize, and analyze data by conducting an experiment to time how long it takes a varying number of students to perform the wave. Students will construct a **scatterplot**, use the plot to look for patterns in the data, and draw a line to summarize the data.

GAISE Components

This investigation follows the four components of statistical problem solving put forth in the *Guidelines for Assessment and Instruction in Statistics Education (GAISE) Report.* The four components are formulate a statistical question that can be answered with data, design and implement a plan to collect appropriate data, analyze the collected data by graphical and numerical methods, and interpret the results of the analysis in the context of the original question. This is a GAISE Level B activity.

Learning Goals

Students will be able to do the following after completing this investigation:

- Construct a scatterplot

- Describe a relationship between two variables

- Draw a line and describe the rate of change

Common Core State Standards for Mathematical Practice

1. Make sense of problems and persevere in solving them.
2. Reason abstractly and quantitatively.
3. Construct viable arguments and critique the reasoning of others.
4. Model with mathematics.

Common Core State Standards
Grade Level Content

8.SP1 Construct and interpret scatterplots for bivariate measurement data to investigate patterns of association between two quantities. Describe patterns such as clustering, outliers, positive or negative association, linear association, and nonlinear association.

8.SP2 Know that straight lines are widely used to model relationships between two quantitative variables. For scatterplots that suggest a linear association, informally fit a straight line, and informally assess the model fit by judging the closeness of the data points to the line.

NCTM Principles and Standards
for School Mathematics

Data Analysis and Probability

Grades 6-8 Students should formulate questions, design studies, and collect data about a characteristic shared by two populations or different characteristics within one population; select, create, and use appropriate graphical representations of data, including histograms, boxplots, and scatterplots.

Materials

- Stopwatch
- Graph paper for each student
- Ruler or straightedge for each student
- Data collection sheet (available on the CD)

Estimated Time

One day

Instructional Plan

✏ Formulate a Statistical Question

1. Begin this investigation by asking your students if they have ever been at a sporting event where the crowd performed the wave. Note that you may wish to show a YouTube video of spectators at a sporting event performing the wave. Share with your students that some people claim the wave was first performed at Fenway Park in Boston. Others claim it originated

at Pacific Lutheran University in the early 1960s. But no matter where it started, it occurs at many sporting events. Ask your students how they might predict how long it takes to perform the wave in a large football stadium. Ask your students what they would need to know to answer this question. Students usually suggest the number of people, number of sections in the stadium, and how fast the wave was performed.

2. After discussing your students' ideas, lead them to the statistical question, "Is there a relationship between number of people and length of time it takes them to perform the wave?"

✎ Collect Appropriate Data

1. Before collecting data, discuss with your students how they are to perform the wave. Suggest they remain seated, but push their chair away from their desk. To perform the wave, they are to stand while raising their arms straight up in the air over their head, and sit back down. Have one student demonstrate the wave. Also, have your students agree on how fast they are to perform the wave. Should each student perform the wave as fast as possible or be deliberate in the motion? It is recommended to have your students be deliberate in the wave motion. It also is recommended that each student practice performing the wave to keep the procedure the same.

2. Appoint a timekeeper. The same person should do all the timing.

3. Start with three students as your first group to perform the wave. When the timekeeper says "go," the first student stands, moves his/her arms, then sits down. As soon as the first person sits down, the second student starts the wave. When the second student sits down, the third student performs the wave. Record the number of students who performed the wave and the time elapsed in Table 5.3.1.

Table 5.3.1 Data Collection Sheet

Number of Students	Time (sec) to Complete the Wave
3	
6	
9	
…	

4. Add three more students and have all six students perform the wave. Again, record the results. Continue to add three students until the entire

class has been included in performing the wave. Table 5.3.2 shows the results of 24 8th-graders having performed the wave experiment.

Table 5.3.2 Results of the Wave Experiment for a Group of 8th-Graders

Number of Students	Time (sec)
3	4
6	8
9	13
12	17
15	20
18	24
21	27
24	30

✏ Analyze the Data

1. Ask your students if they see any patterns in the table. Students should recognize that the number of students increased by three and the time increase varied by 3, 4, or 5 seconds. To help the students focus on the change in time for the wave, add a column to the data collection sheet labeled Change in Time. Table 5.3.3 shows how the time increased as the number of students increased. Ask your students why they think the change in time varied.

Table 5.3.3 Change in Time

Number of Students	Time (sec)	Change in Time
3	4	
6	8	4
9	13	5
12	17	4
15	20	3
18	24	4
21	27	3
24	30	3

2. Ask your students to find the median number of seconds by which the change in time increased. In the example, the median is 4 seconds.

3. Ask your students about how much longer it takes to perform the wave for every additional three people. See if they realize you are asking them for a rate of change, or slope if the data turn out to be linear. For this

example, the median increase is 4 seconds for three people, or 4/3 second increase per person.

4. Ask your students how long it would take all the students in grades 6, 7, and 8 to perform the wave based on the 4/3 second per person estimate.

5. Explain to your students that a scatterplot is also useful in finding patterns or relationships between the number of students and the time to perform the wave. Have your students make a scatterplot on their graph paper. Put Number of Students on the horizontal axis (x-axis) and Length of Time on the vertical (or y) axis. Plot the ordered pairs (number of students, time). Figure 5.3.1 is a scatterplot for the example 8th-grade class data.

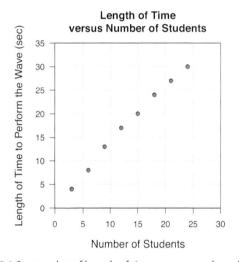

Figure 5.3.1 Scatterplot of length of time versus number of students

6. Have your students examine the scatterplot. Ask your students to describe what they observe from the scatterplot. Ask what type of relationship there is between the number of people and the length of time. And how strong is this relationship? Note that you may wish to have your students find the QCR (Quadrant Count Ratio) described in Investigation 5.2.

7. Explain to your students that you would like for them to draw a straight line through the data matching the pattern in the data as closely as they can. This line will be used to help look for patterns and make predictions about how long the wave takes. Ask them for criteria to use for determining their line. Ask them to justify why they want their line to go through or not go through the origin (0,0). Have them use a straightedge or ruler to draw the line. Figure 5.3.2 shows an example of a line drawn through (0,0) on the scatterplot from the example 8th-grade class data.

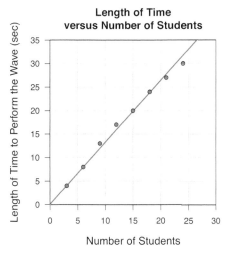

Length of Time versus Number of Students

Figure 5.3.2 Scatterplot with line drawn through the (0,0)

8. Have your students locate a point on the line they drew. For this eyeball line example, a point on the line is (20,26). Ask your students what the coordinates of the ordered pair they listed represent.

9. Using the line that was drawn in Figure 5.3.2, ask your students to describe how much longer it takes to perform the wave for each additional person added. Remind them of the question you asked them in Step 3 of the Analyze the Data section. Tell your students that this value is called a **rate of change** or the **slope** of their line. For this example, the rate of change is 26/20, or about 1.3, which means that for every additional person, the time to perform the wave will increase by about 1.3 seconds.

✏ Interpret the Results in the Context of the Original Question

Have your students recall the original statistical question: "Is there a relationship between the number of people and the length of time to perform the wave?" Have your students answer this question in a paragraph in which they support their answers in depth using the analysis they performed. In this answer, they should refer to the relationship they observed between the number of people performing the wave and the length of time to complete the wave.

Example of 'Interpret the Results' 💿

Note: The following is not an example of actual student work, but an example of all the parts that should be included in student work.

This activity was really fun because we got to perform the wave in class. The statistical question we came up with was "Is there a relationship between the number of people and the length of time to perform the wave?" We actually collected data in our classroom, starting with timing how long it took three of us to perform the wave.

First, we all had to practice so we were doing the procedure the same. Otherwise, we would bias our data. We also had one timekeeper maintain all the times so no bias would enter there, either. We made a data chart by increasing the number of us performing the wave by three each time and the time it took us. We calculated that it took a median increased time of 4 seconds for every three students we added, so the rate of change is an increase of 4/3 seconds for every additional person. We also figured out that if our whole grade level of 243 students lined up to perform the wave and our rate of change was accurate, it would take 243*(4/3) = 324 seconds or about 5.4 minutes to perform the wave. Wow. We showed our data in another way by graphing the points in a scatterplot. Here it is.

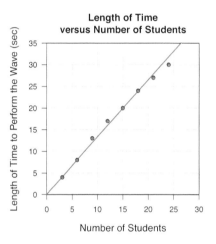

We eyeballed a line through the data. We decided the line should go through the origin because it made sense that if there are no people, then the time to perform the wave is 0. We calculated a rate of change by finding a point that was on our line. The point (20,26) looked like it was on our line. So, the rate of change or slope is 26/20 = 1.3, which is about what we got before for the rate of change, 4/3. This rate means that for every additional person added, the time to perform the wave goes up about 1.3 seconds.

Assessment with Answers 💿

A group of 8th-grade students wanted to investigate the relationship between how long it takes to perform the wave and the number of people participating. The table below shows the results of an experiment that students conducted.

The experiment started with a group of five students. The timer said "Go" and the five students made a wave. The first student stood up, threw his/her hands in the air, turned around, and sat down. The second student did the same, and so on. The last student said "Stop" when he/she sat down. The timer recorded the elapsed time in seconds. The experiment was repeated with 9, 13, 17, 21, and 25 students.

Table 5.3.4 Number of Students and Length of Time to Perform the Wave

Number of Students	Time (sec)
5	16
9	28
13	42
17	54
21	66
25	78

1. Draw a scatterplot of the length of time (sec) versus the number of students.

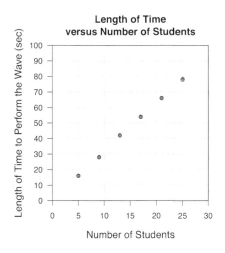

2. Is there a relationship between the number of students and the length of time to perform the wave? Describe the relationship. There is a strong positive relationship.

3. Describe any patterns you observe in the collected data for both the number of students and the length of time. As the number of students increases by four, the time to perform the wave increases by 12.4 seconds (the average of the increase changes in time).

4. Draw a line that matches the pattern in the data as closely as you can. List an ordered pair that lies on the line. Describe what the coordinates of the ordered pair represent.

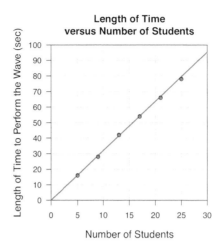

The x-coordinate is the number of people and the y-coordinate is the predicted length of time to perform the wave for that number of people.

5. For each additional student added, how much longer does it take to perform the wave? Use words, numbers, and/or graphs to explain your answer. For each additional student, the wave would take a little more than 3 seconds. In the chart, the change of time for each addition of four students was about 12 seconds, which would give about 3 seconds for each additional person. The rate of change of the line on the graph is about 3.2 seconds per person.

Extension

1. Ask your students to write the equation of the line they drew through the scatterplot of Time versus Number of Students. Ask them to interpret the slope of the line in terms of the scenario.

2. Have your students predict how long it would take all the students in your school to perform the wave. Ask the principal if this could be done during an all-school program.

3. Investigate the size of a stadium near or in your community. Write down how many sections there are and how many seats are in a row. Have your students calculate how long they would predict it would take the spectators to perform the wave at the stadium.

References

Franklin, C., G. Kader, D. Mewborn, J. Moreno, R. Peck, M. Perry, and R. Scheaffer. 2007. *Guidelines for assessment and instruction in statistics education (GAISE) report: A pre-k–12 curriculum framework*. Alexandria, VA: American Statistical Association. *www.amstat.org/education/gaise*.

National Council of Teachers of Mathematics. 2000. *Principles and standards for school mathematics*. Reston, VA: National Council of Teachers of Mathematics.

Common Core State Standards for Mathematics, www.corestandards.org.

Wikipedia, *http://en.wikipedia.org/wiki/wave_(audience)*.

Investigation 5.4
How Do Events Change Over Time?

Overview

Analyzing trends in events that occur over time is important for people who work in government, business, and industry—and for people who study climate, the environment, or agriculture. This investigation explores ways different events change over time and develops the mathematics necessary to describe and analyze the changes. Statistics concepts include the GAISE model and graphing with a scatterplot; mathematics concepts include finding the equation of a line and interpreting its **slope** and **intercept**, as well as **rate of change.** This investigation is based on an activity in *Exploring Linear Relations*, a module in the Data-Driven Mathematics series (1998).

GAISE Components

This investigation follows the four components of statistical problem solving put forth in the *Guidelines for Assessment and Instruction in Statistics Education (GAISE) Report.* The four components are formulate a statistical question that can be answered with data, design and implement a plan to collect appropriate data, analyze the collected data by graphical and numerical methods, and interpret the results of the analysis in the context of the original question. This is a GAISE Level B activity.

Learning Goals

Students will be able to do the following after completing this investigation:

- Find and interpret slope as a rate of change

- Write the equation of a line from given information

- Graph a linear equation

- Make and interpret a scatterplot over time

Common Core State Standards for Mathematical Practices

1. Make sense of problems and persevere in solving them.
2. Reason abstractly and quantitatively.
3. Construct viable arguments and critique the reasoning of others.
4. Model with mathematics.
6. Attend to precision.

Common Core State Standard
Grade Level Content

8.F.3 Interpret the equation y = mx + b as defining a linear function, whose graphics form a straight line; give examples of functions that are not linear.

8.F.4 Construct a function to model a linear relationship between two quantities. Determine the rate of change and initial value of the function from a description of a relationship or from two (x,y) values, including reading these from a table or graph; interpret the rate of change and initial value of a linear function in terms of the situation it models and its graph or a table of values.

8.SP.2 Know that straight lines are widely used to model relationships between two quantitative variables. For scatterplots that suggest a linear association, informally fit a straight line and informally assess the model fit by judging the closeness of the data points to the line.

8.SP.3 Use the equation of a linear model to solve problems in the context of bivariate measurement data, interpreting the slope and intercept.

NCTM Principles and Standards for School Mathematics
Data Analysis and Probability Standard

Grades 6-8 All students should formulate questions, design studies, and collect data about a characteristic shared by two populations or different characteristics within one population; select, create, and use appropriate graphical representations of data, including histograms, boxplots, and scatterplots; make conjectures about possible relationships between two characteristics of a sample on the basis of scatterplots of the data and approximate lines of fit.

Materials

- Table of top three money-making movies for each year from 2000–2010 for each student (available on the CD)
- One sheet of graph paper for each student

Estimated Time

Two days

Instructional Plan

✏ Formulate a Statistical Question

1. Begin the investigation by asking students how they think the cost of

popcorn at the movies has changed over time. Share with your students that a small bag of popcorn cost $0.05 in 1929 and an average of $4.75 in 2011. Much changes over time. Post the list of questions (available on CD) below and ask students to describe the changes over time.

a. How does the cost of buying groceries change over time? How about for gasoline? Cars?

b. How do middle-school students' heights change from year to year?

c. How does the number of cell phones in use change over time?

d. How does the amount of lead in the air change over time?

e. How does the number of 13- and 14-year-olds in the United States change over time?

f. How does the total revenue for fast-food restaurants change over time?

g. How does the TV rating of viewers watching *American Idol* change over time?

h. How does the temperature in your city change from January to December?

2. After discussing the questions, tell your students they will be analyzing data to help answer the statistical question, "By how much, if any, are the mean gross receipts for movies changing over time."

✏ Collect Appropriate Data

1. Discuss with your students that there are questions that need to be considered before collecting data. For example:

• Are the box office receipts only for the United States, or are international receipts also included?

• Are the data to be collected for only the highest-grossing movie of the year or, say, an average of the top 10 movies per year?

• Should the question be for all movies, regardless of category, or restricted to a specific type, such as "action?"

This investigation is based on receipts for the top three grossing movies for each of the years from 2000–2010 and taking the mean of these three receipts per year as data.

2. Ask your students to find the three top money-making movies for each year from 2000–2010 and present the data in a table. Have them find the mean of the three movies for each year and present their results in

a table. Data may be found at *www.imdb.com/boxoffice/alltimegross* or in Table 5.4.1. Note that the gross receipts data are in millions of dollars. The Mean column of entries shown here is for the teacher. Students are to compute it. There is an activity sheet for students on the CD.

Table 5.4.1 Top Three Money-Making Movies for Years 2000–2010 in Millions of Dollars

Year	First	Second	Third	Mean
2010	415.0 Toy Story 3	334.2 Alice in Wonderland	312.1 Iron Man 2	353.8
2009	760.5 Avatar	402.1 Transformers: Revenge of the Fallen	302.0 Harry Potter and the Half-Blood Prince	488.2
2008	533.3 The Dark Knight	318.3 Iron Man	317.0 Indiana Jones and the Kingdom of the Crystal Skull	389.5
2007	336.5 Spider-Man 3	320.7 Shrek the Third	318.8 Transformers	325.3
2006	423.0 Pirates of the Caribbean: Dead Man's Chest	250.9 Night at the Museum	244.1 Cars	306.0
2005	380.3 Star Wars: Episode III – Revenge of the Sith	291.7 The Chronicles of Narnia: The Lion, The Witch, and the Wardrobe	290.0 Harry Potter and the Goblet of Fire	320.7
2004	436.5 Shrek 2	373.4 Spider-Man 2	370.3 The Passion of the Christ	393.4
2003	377.0 The Lord of the Rings: The Return of the King	339.7 Finding Nemo	305.4 Pirates of the Caribbean: The Curse of the Black Pearl	340.7
2002	403.7 Spider-Man	340.5 The Lord of the Rings: The Two Towers	310.7 Star Wars: Episode II – Attack of the Clones	351.6
2001	317.6 Harry Potter and the Sorcerer's Stone	313.8 The Lord of the Rings: The Fellowship of the Ring	267.7 Shrek	299.7
2000	260.0 How the Grinch Stole Christmas	233.6 Cast Away	215.4 Mission: Impossible II	236.3

Analyze the Data

1. Ask your students how much money Toy Story 3 grossed in 2010.

2. Ask your students which is the highest-grossing movie in all the years listed? How much money did the movie gross?

3. Ask your students what trends they observe in the data. Hopefully, they will suggest that a graph would be helpful in answering the question.

4. Have your students construct a **scatterplot**. The scatterplot can help visualize if and to what extent there is a relationship between year and mean gross receipts. Students should place the Year variable on the horizontal axis and the Mean Gross Receipts variable on the vertical axis. Note that a scatterplot with time on the horizontal is often called a **time series** plot. The plot is shown in Figure 5.4.1. Note also that a time series plot has only one data point per year, so the graph is realistically of a single numerical variable (vertical axis).

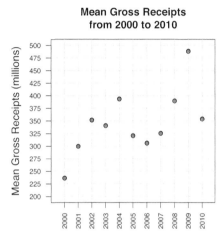

Figure 5.4.1 Time series plot of mean gross receipts (in millions) from 2000–2010

5. Ask your students if it generally appears that the mean gross receipts have increased over the years 2000–2010?

6. Ask your students if there are any years in which the mean receipts decreased from the previous year? How can these situations be identified on the graph?

7. Discuss with your students that to help visualize any increases and decreases in mean gross receipts, it would be helpful to find the change from one year to the next. Display Table 5.4.2 and explain that the change of 63.4 million dollars for the years 2000–2001 was determined by subtracting 236.3 (mean for 2000) from 299.7 (mean for 2001).

8. Ask your students how they would find the change for the years 2009–2010. Ask them why this value is a negative number.

9. Have your students complete the rest of Table 5.4.2.

Table 5.4.2 Change in Mean Gross Receipts

	2000–2001	2001–2002	2002–2003	2003–2004	2004–2005
Mean Change (millions)	+63.4				
	2005–2006	2006–2007	2007–2008	2008–2009	2009–2010
Mean Change (millions)					-134.4

The mean change for all the years is listed in Table 5.4.3.

Table 5.4.3 Change in Mean Gross Receipts (Completed Table)

	2000–2001	2001–2002	2002–2003	2003–2004	2004–2005
Mean Change (millions)	+63.4	+51.9	-10.9	+52.7	-72.7
	2005–2006	2006–2007	2007–2008	2008–2009	2009–2010
Mean Change (millions)	-14.7	+19.3	+64.2	+98.7	-134.4

10. Ask your students to find the mean of the changes in gross receipts for all years between 2000–2001 and 2009–2010. Remind students to be aware of the negative numbers when finding the sum of the changes.

11. Discuss with your students what the mean of the changes represents. **Note:** The mean represents the amount that the gross receipts would change each year if the change were a constant. In this case, the gross receipts go up an average of $11.75 million each year.

12. Show your students a different method for finding the mean of the changes by taking the overall increase in gross receipts between 2000–2010 and dividing it by 10. **Note:** (353.8 – 236.3)/10 = $11.75 million. Recall that the top three money-making movies in 2010 grossed $353.8 million and the top three money-making movies in 2000 grossed $236.3 million.

13. Discuss with your students why the two procedures result in the same value.

14. Have your students assume that mean gross receipts increased by the constant amount of $11.75 million per year. Using that assumption, ask them to estimate what the mean gross receipts in 2001 would have been. Note that 236.3 + 11.75 = 248.05 million.

15. Assuming a constant increase of 11.75 every year, complete Table 5.4.4.

Table 5.4.4 Estimated Mean Gross Receipts
(Assuming a Constant Increase)

Estimated Mean Gross Receipts (Assuming a Constant Increase in Receipts from Year to Year)					
Year	2000	2001	2002	2003	2004	2005
Time	236.3					
Year	2006	2007	2008	2009	2010	
Time						

The estimated mean gross receipts assuming a constant are shown in Table 5.4.5.

Table 5.4.5 Complete Table of the Estimated Mean Gross
Receipts (Assuming a Constant Increase)

Estimated Mean Gross Receipts (Assuming a Constant Increase in Receipts from Year to Year)					
Year	2000	2001	2002	2003	2004	2005
Time	236.3	248.05	259.8	271.55	283.3	295.05
Year	2006	2007	2008	2009	2010	
Time	306.8	318.55	330.3	342.05	353.8	

16. For the estimated mean gross receipts assuming a constant increase, have your students construct a scatterplot with Year on the horizontal axis and Mean Gross Receipts on the vertical axis. See Figure 5.4.2.

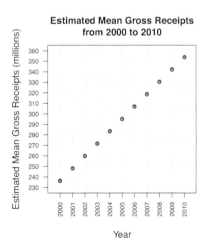

Figure 5.4.2 Time series plot of estimated mean gross receipts for 2000–2010 (assuming a constant change)

17. Ask your students to describe the pattern of the points they see in the graph. **Note:** The constant change in mean gross receipts over time is called the **rate of change.** When the rate of change is constant for equal

time intervals, the graph of the relationship is a straight line. The rate of change is also referred to as the **slope** of the line.

18. Now that your students have been reminded as to what rate of change or slope means for linear data, using the **original data** and the scatterplot of the original data, have your students choose two points so a line through them would be a fairly good prediction line in their view. For example, the line through (2001, 299.7) and (2008, 389.5) appears to fit the data well. Using those two points, discuss how to find the rate of change and how to interpret the result in the context of the problem. Then, have your students do the calculation and interpretation. **Note:** The rate of change of mean gross receipts as determined by the data from 2001–2008 is (389.5 − 299.7) / (2008 − 2001) = 89.8 / 7 = 12.83 million dollars. In words, a possible interpretation of the slope in context might be: For each one-year increase, the mean gross receipts increase by $12.83 million, on average. The time series plot with a trend line appears in Figure 5.4.3.

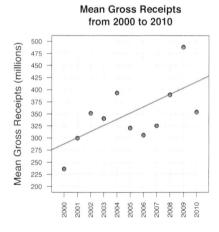

Figure 5.4.3 Time series plot of estimated mean gross receipts from 2000–2010 with trend line

19. Discuss with your students the comparison between the rate of change of 11.75 when a constant rate of change was assumed and the rate of change of 12.83 when using the original data from 2001 and 2008. This is key to this investigation. Ask your students how well they think the line drawn describes the data. Discuss what the line with slope $11.75 million is based on as compared to the line they drew with a slope of 12.83. Which is better? Note that the Common Core State Standards in statistics at the high-school level develop a more formal structure with criteria for determining a best-fitting prediction line.

✏ Interpret the Results in the Context of the Original Question

1. Place students into groups of three. Ask each group to discuss their answer to the original question, "By how much, if any, are the average gross receipts for movies increasing over time?"

    Each group should prepare a report on their findings. Your students' report should be based on the data collected, their scatterplots, and the rate of change. The report should include key calculations and graphs.

2. Ask your students if they think the trend they observed in the scatterplot will continue. Ask them to predict what the mean gross receipts for the top three movies will be in 2011. Ask them how close their prediction is to the actual mean. Why did they not match? **Note:** From Figure 5.4.3, a reasonable prediction would be $425 million. The actual results were Harry Potter and Deathly Hallows Part 2, $381.0; Transformers: Death of the Moor, $352.4; and The Twilight Saga: Breaking Dawn Part 1, $280.3. The mean of these top three grossing movies is $337.90.

Example of 'Interpret the Results'

Note: The following is not an example of actual student work, but an example of all the parts that should be included in student work.

In our communications class last week, we were looking at old silent movies and comparing them to the high-tech ones of today. We were wondering how much movies make. We decided that a neat question to investigate in our mathematics class would be, "By how much, if any, are the average gross receipts for movies increasing over time?" From a website, we found a listing of gross receipts for movies year by year. We decided to look at the top three money-making films for the years 2000–2010 and then take the mean of the three to use as our data. The data are in millions of dollars by the way. To see if there was any relationship or trend, we drew a scatterplot, which is called a time series plot since time would be on the horizontal axis. Here is our plot:

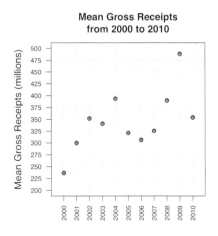

We concluded from the graph that there is a positive relationship between time and mean gross receipts. That means, as we look at years from 2000 going up to 2010, mean gross receipts for those years generally increase. Of course, in some years, receipts went down, but overall there was an upward trend. To see the ups and downs, we calculated them and then found their mean. The average change in mean gross receipts was $11.75 million. In words, if the gross receipts changed a constant amount from year to year between 2000–2010, then that constant amount would be $11.75 million. So, we also looked at this by saying that if all our data points fell on a straight line exactly, then the slope of that line would be 11.75. Here's a graph of what that constant situation would look like:

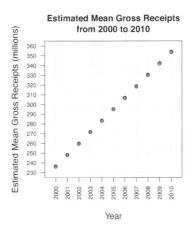

But, of course, our real data did not fall on a straight line. So, as a final part of our analysis, we looked at our original data in its plot and drew a line through the data that we thought would fit the data pretty well. We went through the points and picked on (2001, 299.7) and (2008, 389.5). Here is the plot with our prediction line on it:

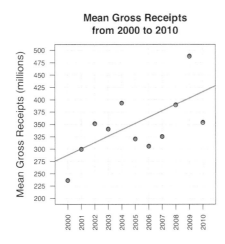

The slope for our estimated real data line was (389.5 − 299.7) / (2008 − 2001) = $12.83 million. It is higher than the average one of $11.75 million. It's kind of hard to say which method is right. The constant method averaged over the ups and downs, which smoothed things over. The picking two points method is very dependent on which points were chosen, but we think we did a good job because, looking at the graph, the line balances the points fairly well. So, we like our two-point method better.

To use our line to predict what mean gross receipts might be in 2011, we see from the graph that a prediction would be around $425 million. To be more correct, our slope is $12.83 increase per year. We know that (2008,389.5) lies on our line. Since 2011 is three years from 2008, our prediction for 2011 is 389.5 + 3*12.83 = $427.99 million.

We checked the website and found that the actual top movies in 2011 grossed a mean of $337.90, considerably less than our prediction. One reason is that the economy is not very good and people don't have as much money to spend on going out.

Assessment with Answers

A group of students was interested in answering the question, "By how much have the winning times of the past 15 Olympic Games men's 100-meter dash decreased? Table 5.4.6 shows the data they collected for the years 1952–2008.

Table 5.4.6 Winning Times for Men's Olympic 100-Meter Dash

Winning Times (seconds) - Olympic Games 100-Meter Dash – Men							
Year	1952	1956	1960	1964	1968	1972	1976
Time	10.40	10.50	10.20	10.00	9.95	10.14	10.06
Year	1980	1984	1988	1992	1996	2000	2004	2008
Time	10.25	9.99	9.92	9.96	9.84	9.87	9.85	9.69

Note that, in 1992, the original winner was Ben Johnson of Canada, who ran the dash in 9.79 s, but he was stripped of the medal after testing positive for steroid use. Figure 5.4.4 is a time series plot with the year on the horizontal axis and the dash time on the y-axis.

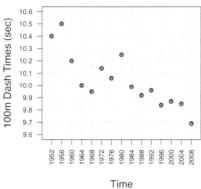

Figure 5.4.4 Time series plot of men's Olympic 100 m dash winning times for 1952–2008

Write a report starting with answering the question, "By how much have the winning times of the past 15 Olympic Games men's 100-meter dash decreased?" Include the following:

- A description of the trend you observe in the data. The trend in the winning times for the 100-meter dash has been decreasing.

- Identification of the years in which the Olympic 100-meter time was higher than the previous Olympic 100-meter time. In 1956 and in 1980, the winning times were higher than the previous Olympic 100-meter time.

- An appropriate graph with a line drawn through the points (1952, 10.4) and (2008, 9.69) and, by using these two points, the rate of change of the Olympic 100-meter times. The rate of change is -0.01. See Figure 5.4.5.

- A written explanation of what the rate of change of the times represents in the context of this investigation. A rate of change of -0.01 means that the winning time for the 100-meter dash decreases by about 0.01 seconds every year. Or, the rate of change of -0.01 means that every Olympics (four years), the winning time for the 100-meter dash decreases by about 0.04 seconds.

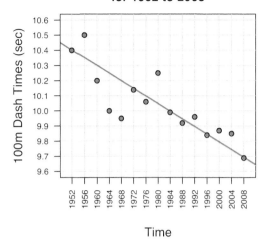

Olympic 100m Dash Winning Times
for 1952 to 2008

Figure 5.4.5 Time series plot of men's Olympic 100 m dash
winning times for 1952–2008 with trend line

Extension

This investigation can be extended into developing the equation of a line. Develop the equation of the line your students drew through the points (2001, 299.7) and (2008, 389.5). They should find the rate of change (slope) and write the equation in point-slope form. Then, they should find the y-intercept and interpret this value. Students also could write the equation of the line in slope-intercept form and discuss the usefulness of the y-intercept in this problem.

References

Burrill, G., and P. Hopfensperger. 1998. *Exploring linear relations*. New York, NY: Dale Seymour.

Franklin, C., G. Kader, D. Mewborn, J. Moreno, R. Peck, M. Perry, and R. Scheaffer. 2007. *Guidelines for assessment and instruction in statistics education (GAISE) report: A pre-k–12 curriculum framework*. Alexandria, VA: American Statistical Association. *www.amstat.org/education/gaise*.

National Council of Teachers of Mathematics. 2000. *Principles and standards for school mathematics*. Reston, VA: National Council of Teachers of Mathematics.

Common Core State Standards for Mathematics, *www.corestandards.org*.

IMDb, *www.imdb.com/boxoffice/alltimegross*.

INVESTIGATING PROBABILITY

INVESTIGATION 6.1
HOW LIKELY IS IT?

Overview

This investigation introduces students to basic concepts of **probability,** the mathematics of chance events**.** Examples of **random events** and a method for evaluating the chance they will occur are presented. Specifically, students will begin by discussing events in their lives that are **certain**, **likely**, **neither likely nor unlikely**, **unlikely,** and **impossible** to happen. This will enable them to develop a personal or subjective sense of probability—a measure of how likely an event is to occur. They will then be introduced to the idea of assigning a number from 0 to 1 to the terms certain, likely, neither likely nor unlikely, unlikely, and impossible. Students will use a "walk-on probability scale" to gather and record data on the probability of common events in their lives. This investigation is based on an activity in *Exploring Statistics in the Elementary Grades* by Carolyn Bereska, L. Carey Bolster, Cyrilla A. Bolster, and Richard Scheaffer.

GAISE Components

This investigation follows the four components of statistical problem solving put forth in the *Guidelines for Assessment and Instruction in Statistics Education (GAISE) Report.* The four components are formulate a statistical question that can be answered with data, design and implement a plan to collect appropriate data, analyze the collected data by graphical and numerical methods, and interpret the results of the analysis in the context of the original question. This is a GAISE Level A activity.

Learning Goals

Students will be able to do the following after completing this investigation:

- Use the terms certain, likely, unlikely, and impossible correctly

- Associate the chances of occurrence of an event with a position on a probability scale

Common Core State Standards
for Mathematical Practice

1. Make sense of problems and persevere in solving them
2. Reason abstractly or quantitatively

3. Construct viable arguments and critique the reasoning of others
4. Model with mathematics

Common Core State Standards
Grade Level Content

7.SP.5 Understand that the probability of a chance event is a number between 0 and 1 that expresses the likelihood of the event occurring. Larger numbers indicate greater likelihood. A probability near 0 indicates an unlikely event, a probability around 1/2 indicates an event that is neither unlikely nor likely, and a probability near 1 indicates a likely event.

NCTM Principles and Standards
for School Mathematics

Data Analysis and Probability

Pre-K–2 All students should discuss events related to students' experiences as likely or unlikely.

Grades 3–5 All students should describe events as likely or unlikely and discuss the degree of likelihood using such words as certain, equally likely, and impossible; predict the probability of outcomes of simple experiments and test the predictions; understand that the measure of the likelihood of an event can be represented by a number from 0 to 1.

Materials

- Masking tape and marker to create a walk-on probability scale
- Table 6.1.1 Chance Events (available on the CD)
- "What are the Chances?" Worksheet 6.1.2 for each student (available on the CD)

Estimated Time

One day

Instructional Plan

✏ Formulate a Statistical/Probabilistic Question

1. Begin this investigation by asking your students if they know what the word "impossible" means. Ask them for several examples of events that

would be impossible for them to perform, such as run a mile in three minutes, build a tower of blocks 100 feet tall, or eat 500 hamburgers in one sitting. Ask them for several examples of events they are certain they can perform, such as add 2 + 2 correctly or write their name. Ask your students to name several events that are between being impossible and certain for them to do, such as doing a jumping rope five times in a row without missing or tossing a wad of paper in a basket six feet away. Explain that, often times, when playing a game like Candy Land or Chutes and Ladders, it is hard to tell what is going to happen. Many games have a spinner, number cube, or other device that gives the number of spaces to move in a turn. Ask your students if they know what the spinner will land on before they spin. Tell your students that they will be exploring events whose actual outcomes they can't always be absolutely certain will happen. Explain to them that such events are referred to as **chance events**. Lead them to the statistical/probabilistic question, "How likely is it for each chance event in a list to happen: impossible to happen, unlikely to happen, neither unlikely nor likely to happen, likely to happen, or certain to happen?"

2. Display Table 6.1.1 and ask your students to review the list of chance events. They need to classify each as being impossible to occur, unlikely to occur, neither unlikely nor likely to occur, likely to occur, or certain to occur.

Table 6.1.1 Chance Events

Classify each of these chance events as being impossible to occur, unlikely to occur, neither unlikely nor likely to occur, likely to occur, or certain to occur.

   a. The class will watch TV in school today.

   b. We will all use computers sometime today.

   c. We will have lunch today.

   d. The class will be in school on Saturday.

   e. The class will go to the movies this week.

   f. We will go outside for recess today.

   g. If the teacher were to put the names of all the students in our class in a hat and draw one name, a boy's name will be chosen.

   h. If I have a bag of 10 blue cubes and one red cube and draw one cube, the red cube will be drawn.

✏ Collect Appropriate Data

1. Place your students into groups of three or four and give them a recording sheet labeled as follows (available on the CD):

Impossible	Unlikely	Neither Unlikely nor Likely	Likely	Certain

Have each group decide how likely each of the eight chance events in Table 6.1.1 will occur by placing each event under impossible, unlikely, neither unlikely nor likely, likely, or certain. An example is shown in Figure 6.1.1. Note that it might be easier for some students if the chance events are printed on pieces of paper, one per piece, so they can simply move them around to the correct column.

Impossible	Unlikely	Neither Unlikely nor Likely	Likely	Certain
Saturday school Go to movie	Red cube drawn	Draw boy's name	Watch TV Recess outside	Use computers Lunch

Figure 6.1.1 Chance events

2. Ask your students to name other chance events that would fit under impossible, unlikely, neither unlikely nor likely, likely, or certain. Have them add their chance events to the list and explain some of their suggestions to the class as a whole.

✏ Analyze the Data

1. Explain to your students that they have given a <u>word</u> classification to how likely certain chance events are to occur. Lead the discussion to the idea of probability as a method for assigning a <u>number</u> to the words impossible, unlikely, neither unlikely nor likely, likely, certain. On the board, draw the probability scale as shown in Figure 6.1.2. Explain that 0 means there is no chance of occurring, or impossible, and 1 means certain to occur. Place the word unlikely halfway between impossible and the middle,

and place the word likely halfway between the middle and certain. Explain that ½ is halfway between the 0 and 1 and would represent "neither unlikely nor likely."

Figure 6.1.2 Probability scale on a number line

2. Place your students in groups of four and give each group a probability scale handout. Ask the students to write the events in their list (the original ones plus the ones they added) on the probability scale. Figure 6.1.3 shows how one class placed the chance events on the probability scale.

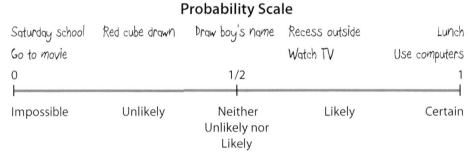

Figure 6.1.3 Sample class results on the probability scale

3. Place a long piece of tape on the floor to make a "walk-on probability scale." Label the piece of tape as shown in Figure 6.1.4.

Figure 6.1.4 Walk-on probability scale

216

For each event or another event that could give different results (e.g., How likely is it that you will be able to jump a jump rope 20 times in a row?), have each of your students stand on the place in the scale that corresponds to their idea about the chance of that particular event occurring.

For many of the events, students will stand in different places on the scale. Have your students identify which events prompted all students to stand in the same place and which prompted students to stand in difference places. Discuss possible reasons for each standing arrangement.

Note that if there is not much variation in their responses, use other chance events such as "How likely is it that your favorite sports team will win their next game?" or "How likely is it that girls are better than boys in shooting free throws?"

✏ Interpret the Results in the Context of the Original Question

Have your students recall that the original statistical/probabilistic question was, "How likely is it for each chance event in a list to happen: impossible to happen, unlikely to happen, neither unlikely nor likely to happen, likely to happen, or certain to happen?" At the start of this investigation, your students shared events they said they couldn't do, some that they were certain they could do, and some events that they were uncertain they could do. Ask your students to summarize what it means for a chance event to be impossible, unlikely, neither unlikely nor likely, likely, or certain to happen. Have them explain their answers using some of the events discussed in this investigation.

Example of 'Interpret the Results' 💿

Note: The following is not an example of actual student work, but an example of all the parts that should be included in student work.

Our teacher asked us to give him examples of things that are impossible for us to do. Impossible means that the event cannot happen. Some of the events we said were hit a baseball 500 feet in the air, fly like a bird, and run 100 miles an hour. He also asked us for events we are certain will happen. These are events that have to happen. Some of us said the sun will rise in the east, I will sit at my school desk today, and I will eat lunch in the lunchroom today. We also talked about events that we were not certain of happening. We said it was likely that we would eat a dessert today and drink milk today, but we said that eating something blue was unlikely because we didn't think it would happen, but it might if someone ate a blue sucker.

After we assigned a word to each of the chance events as to how often we thought they would happen, our teacher had us assign numbers to the events. These numbers are called probabilities. A probability for a chance event is how likely the event will occur. The probability numbers go from 0, which means impossible, to 1, which means certain. So, we assigned 0 to the event that we could run 100 miles an hour, and we assigned 1 to the event the sun will rise in the east. We didn't assign a number to the events we thought were unlikely, but we suggested that they would be between 0 and the middle. The likely ones would be between the middle and 1. Our teacher told us that the halfway number between 0 and 1 is the fraction ½, and it would mean neither unlikely nor likely.

Our teacher put tape on the floor that showed 0, ½, and 1 spread out. All of us in the class stood on the "walk-on probability scale" to show how likely we thought the event "I can jump a jump rope 20 times in a row" would be. It was neat to see that some of us didn't think we could do it. They were down toward 0 and others were spread out between 0 and 1. I was pretty sure I could do it, so I stood about halfway between ½ and 1 on the likely part.

Assessment with Answers

1. Think about each of the following events. Decide where each event would be located on the scale below. Place the letter for each event below on the appropriate place on the scale.

   What are the chances for each event?

   A. The next roll of a fair number cube will be a 2.

   B. You will be successful in four of your next 10 free throw shots.

   C. You will meet a dinosaur on your way home from school.

   D. You will read at least three books this month.

   E. A coin will come up heads five times in a row.

   F. A word chosen randomly from this sentence has four letters.

   G. It will be sunny tomorrow.

   H. You will eat something the color blue today.

   I. A spinner with 10 equal parts numbered 1 through 10 will come up an even number in the next spin.

   J. You will have math homework tonight.

   K. If the names of all the teachers at our school are in a hat, my teacher's name will be picked.

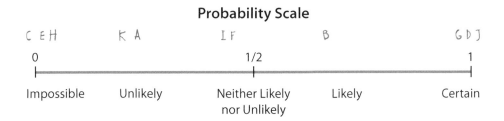

Figure 6.1.5 Sample class results on the probability scale

2. Write two events that are impossible to occur, two that are unlikely to occur, two that are neither unlikely nor likely to occur, two that are likely to occur, and two that are certain to occur. Give reasons for your answers.

Some possible responses:

Impossible
    The president of the USA will visit me at home tomorrow.
    I can fly like a bird.

Unlikely
    The card chosen from a shuffled deck of cards will be a face card.
    There will be a fire drill in school today.

Neither Likely nor Unlikely
    The number rolled on a fair number cube is even.
    The color of a card chosen at random from a deck of cards is red.

Likely
    The result of one spin of a spinner with equal colors red, blue, green, and yellow will be a primary color.
    I will play a video game sometime this week.

Certain
    The sun will rise in the east.
    I will go to bed tonight.

Extension

1. Bring in a board game like Chutes and Ladders or Candyland. Investigate the different outcomes that can occur when playing the game. Ask students to place the outcomes on the probability scale and assign a value of chance for that event to occur.

2. For intermediate students, discuss ways to express probability as percents, fractions, and ratios. What values would they associate with the terms impossible, unlikely, neither unlikely nor likely, likely, and certain? Explain why.

3. Have students use fractions or percents found in newspapers or magazines to make their own scale of likelihood of events.

References

Bereska, C., L. C. Bolster, C. A. Bolster, and R. Scheaffer. 1998. *Exploring statistics in the elementary grades: Book one, grades k–6.* White Plains, NY: Dale Seymour.

Franklin, C., G. Kader, D. Mewborn, J. Moreno, R. Peck, M. Perry, and R. Scheaffer. 2007. *Guidelines for assessment and instruction in statistics education (GAISE) report: A pre-k–12 curriculum framework.* Alexandria, VA: American Statistical Association. *www.amstat.org/education/gaise.*

National Council of Teachers of Mathematics. 2000. *Principles and standards for school mathematics.* Reston, VA: National Council of Teachers of Mathematics.

Common Core State Standards for Mathematics. www.corestandards.org.

INVESTIGATION 6.2
WHAT'S THE CHANCE OF SEEING AN ELEPHANT AT THE ZOO?

Overview

This investigation focuses on introducing students to answering **"how likely"** questions that are based on data collected and presented in a tally chart. This activity combines basic concepts in data collection and **probability** in a science context, identifying and classifying zoo animals in various ways. Students will use a package of zoo animal crackers to sort them according to some criterion, construct a tally chart, graph data in a bar graph, and use the data collected to determine probabilities.

GAISE Components

This investigation follows the four components of statistical problem solving put forth in the *Guidelines for Assessment and Instruction in Statistics Education (GAISE) Report*. The four components are formulate a statistical question that can be answered with data, design and implement a plan to collect appropriate data, analyze the collected data by graphical and numerical methods, and interpret the results of the analysis in the context of the original question. This is a GAISE Level A activity.

Learning Goals

Students will be able to do the following after completing this investigation:

- Demonstrate an ability to sort items, specifically animals, according to likeness

- Display their data in a tally chart/frequency table and illustrate the distribution in a bar graph

- Become familiar with the process of randomly choosing an item from a data set

- Display their result as a fraction of some specific outcome to occur

- Understand basic "how likely" probability terms: least likely, equally likely, most likely Compare probabilities and express one as being more likely or less likely than another to occur

- Recognize and identify categorical data

Science

Students will learn science terms such as claws, hooves, carnivores, herbivores, and omnivores.

Common Core State Standards
for Mathematical Practice

1. Make sense of problems and persevere in solving them.
2. Reason abstractly and quantitatively.
3. Construct viable arguments and critique the reasoning of others.
4. Model with mathematics.

Common Core State Standards
Grade Level Content

6.SP.1 Recognize a statistical question as one that anticipates variability in the data related to the question and accounts for it in the answers.

6.SP.2 Understand that a set of data collected to answer a statistical question has a distribution that can be described by its center, spread, and overall shape.

7.SP.5 Understand that the probability of a chance event is a number between 0 and 1 that expresses the likelihood of the event occurring. Larger numbers indicate greater likelihood. A probability near 0 indicates an unlikely event, a probability around ½ indicates an event that is neither unlikely nor likely, and a probability near 1 indicates a likely event.

7.SP.8a Understand that, just as with simple events, the probability of a compound event is the fraction of outcomes in the sample space for which the compound event occurs.

NCTM Principles and Standards
for School Mathematics

Data Analysis and Probability

Pre-K–2 All students should discuss events related to students' experiences as likely or unlikely.

Grades 3–5 All students should describe events as likely or unlikely and discuss the degree of likelihood using such words as *certain, equally likely*, and *impossible*; understand that the measure of the likelihood of an event can be represented by a number from 0 to 1.

Materials

- One package of Austin Zoo Animal Crackers, a Kellogg product, for each pair of students. Each 2 oz. package contains around 30 crackers. **Note:** Other brands may be used, but the types and quantities of animals may differ from the Austin brand used in this investigation.

- Graph paper (large squares)

Estimated Time

One day

Instructional Plan

✏️ **Formulate a Statistical/Probabilistic Question**

1. Discuss with your students animals they might see in a zoo. Tell them that rather than taking a trip to the zoo, the zoo is coming to them. Give each pair of students a bag of zoo animal crackers. Have them open them and identify the animals represented. Make certain the children do not eat their crackers before completing the activity!

In the Austin Zoo Animal Crackers, there are 12 possible 'zoo' animals: bear, camel, elephant, lion, monkey, mountain goat, owl, penguin, rabbit, rhinoceros, tortoise, and zebra. Figure 6.2.1 shows a picture of the 12 possible animals. Note that each bag may not necessarily contain all 12 species. Also, your students may want to give them other names. For example, the zebra may be labeled a horse. Moreover, they may question whether a rabbit is a zoo animal. Regardless, the class should agree on an assignment of names.

Figure 6.2.1 Twelve animals in Austin Zoo Animal Crackers 💿

224

2. Ask your students what questions they would like to investigate about their zoo. Some questions students might suggest are the following:

   - How many of each type of animal are there in the zoo?

   - What is the class's favorite animal?

   Through a discussion, lead your students to the statistical/probabilistic question, "If an animal were to be chosen at random from a bag of zoo animals, which type of animal would be the most likely or least likely to be chosen?" Note that the randomness requires that each cracker have the same chance of being chosen as does any other cracker.

✏ Collect Appropriate Data

Ask your students to organize their animals (crackers) by stacking animals of the same species on top of each other. The purpose will be to get a count of how many of each animal they have. One way that students may want to organize their animals is a pictograph, in which animals are lined up horizontally and then those of the same species are placed flat on the desk vertically above each other.

Note that animals are often broken in transit. Discuss with your students that it is important they all agree on what to do with the broken crackers. You might suggest the "broken animals" that can be put back together completely might be counted, whereas those that are broken beyond complete recognition are not to be counted. (Those data and only those data at this point in the investigation may be consumed.)

✏ Analyze Data

1. Have each group of students create a tally chart/frequency distribution (available on the CD) for their zoo data set based on a single bag of crackers. **Note:** A frequency distribution is a list of the values (categories or names) of a categorical variable and their frequencies (how many times each occurs). In this example, the categories are animals. Table 6.2.1 shows an example of a frequency distribution constructed by one group of students.

Table 6.2.1 Example of a Frequency Distribution of a 'Zoo'

Name of Animal	Tally	Count/Frequency
Bear	|	1
Camel	||	2
Elephant	||||	4
Lion	|	1
Monkey	ⅢⅠ|	6
Mountain Goat	||	2
Owl	||	2
Penguin	|||	3
Rabbit		0
Rhinoceros	||	2
Tortoise	|||	3
Zebra	||||	4

2. Using the tally chart/frequency table, have your students draw a bar graph using graph paper. Be sure there is an equal amount of space separating the names of the animals listed below the horizontal axis. The vertical scale should be labeled by frequency of animals. Figure 6.2.2 is a bar graph for the example zoo collected by one group of students.

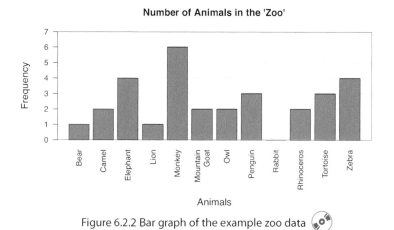

Figure 6.2.2 Bar graph of the example zoo data

Note: Students could make a picture graph. Using large square graph paper, students label each animal type on the horizontal axis like the bar graph example shown. The students then place one animal in each square above the appropriate label. If there were three penguins, then each penguin would be placed in a square above the "Penguin" label. Using the graph paper ensures that the height of each column is the same as the frequency of each animal type so that three penguins occupy the same area space as do three tortoises, for example.

3. Ask your students the following questions:

    a. How many elephants were in their zoo?

    b. Which animal has the most of its kind in the zoo? That animal is called the mode. Note that the monkey is the mode animal in the example.

    c. Which animal has the least of its kind in the zoo?

4. Tell your students to imagine they were to reach into their bag of animals and, without looking, mix up all the animals and then pick out one. Ask your students what animal is the most likely to be drawn out. Discuss how the "most likely" is the animal with the greatest number and the "least likely" is the animal with the smallest number. Note that some students may say the least likely is the rabbit, since there aren't any. Others may argue that the smallest number has to be positive, so the bear or lion would be the smallest number in the example.

5. Combine the class data on the board in a frequency distribution. Make a bar graph of the class data. Figure 6.2.3 shows the results from the whole class.

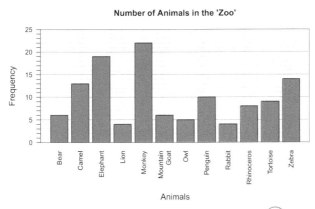

Figure 6.2.3 Bar graph of sample class zoo

6. Ask your students to identify the most likely and least likely animal to be selected at random from a container that would contain all the animals collected in the class. Have them explain their choices.

7. Ask your students to compare the bar graph representing their bag or zoo to the bar graph of the whole class's results.

8. Ask them which animal was most likely to be drawn from their bag and compare their answer to the class's result.

✏ Interpret the Results in the Context of the Original Question

1. Have your students recall the original statistical/probabilistic question, "If an animal were to be chosen at random from a bag of zoo animals, which species would be the most likely or least likely to be chosen?" Ask your students to write an answer to the question and use the class data to justify their answer.

2. Ask students if they think Kellogg makes the same number of each animal in their production of Austin Zoo Animal Crackers.

Example of 'Interpret the Results'

Note: The following is not an example of actual student work, but an example of all the parts that should be included in student work.

Our teacher talked to us about animals in a zoo. We made a list and then our teacher handed out a bag of animal crackers that represented our zoo. We worked in pairs. We investigated the question, "If an animal were to be chosen at random from a bag of zoo animals, which type of animal would be the most likely or least likely to be chosen?" We made a tally chart of the animals in our bag and then made a bar graph. Based on our bar graphs, we decided which animal was most likely by looking at the heights of the bars. The animals that had the highest bars were the ones we thought would be the most likely to be chosen. Also, the animal that occurred the most is called the mode. We combined the results from all the groups. The following bar graph shows our class results:

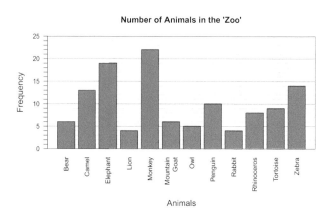

Our class data showed that the monkey was the most likely to be chosen, with the elephant also a good possibility. So the monkey is the mode animal, while the lion, owl, and rabbit were the least likely animals to be chosen. Also, we concluded that Kellogg's does not bake the same number of each animal. If they did, the bars would be more even. Statistics is kind of fun because we were allowed to eat our data when we were done.

Assessment with Answers

Chris sorted a bag of animal crackers and drew the bar graph shown in figure 6.2.4.

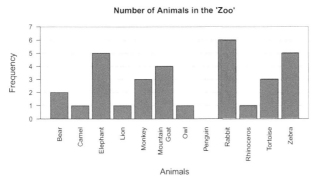

Figure 6.2.4 Bar graph of Chris's zoo

1. How many elephants were in Chris's bag? There were five elephants in Chris's bag.

2. How many rabbits were in Chris's bag? There were six rabbits in Chris's bag.

3. How many more rabbits were in the bag than penguins? There were six rabbits and no penguins, so there were six more rabbits than penguins in Chris's bag.

4. How many more rabbits were in the bag than monkeys? There were three more rabbits than monkeys in Chris's bag.

5. If you reach into Chris's bag and randomly picked out one animal, which animal would:

   Most likely be chosen? The rabbit occurred the most and hence would be the most likely animal chosen.

   Least likely be chosen? Well, if the answer has to be positive, then it is a tie among camel, lion, owl, and rhinoceros. If 0 is allowed, then the least likely would be penguin, since there are no penguins.

Extensions

1. Using the class data, ask your students to calculate the probability of randomly choosing each animal type.

2. Ask what the probability is of randomly choosing:

- An animal with four feet?

- An animal with claws? Hooves?

- An animal with knees?

- A meat-eating animal? A pure carnivorous animal?

- An animal that eats vegetation? A pure herbivorous animal?

- An animal that eats both meat and vegetation? A pure omnivorous animal?

3. Discuss how to draw a Venn diagram. For example, create a Venn diagram identifying the carnivores, herbivores, and omnivores for a package of animal crackers as a class. Then, in groups of two, have students create their own Venn diagram. Figure 6.2.5 is based on different traits chosen by a pair of students.

Figure 6.2.5 Venn diagram of carnivores, herbivores, and omnivores

References

Franklin, C., G. Kader, D. Mewborn, J. Moreno, R. Peck, M. Perry, and R. Scheaffer. 2007. *Guidelines for assessment and instruction in statistics education (GAISE) report: A pre-k–12 curriculum framework*. Alexandria, VA: American Statistical Association. *www.amstat.org/education/gaise*.

National Council of Teachers of Mathematics. 2000. *Principles and standards for school mathematics*. Reston, VA: National Council of Teachers of Mathematics.

Common Core State Standards for Mathematics. www.corestandards.org.

Investigation 6.3
What Do Frogs Eat?

Overview

This investigation introduces students to answering questions about proportionality that leads to a basic understanding of probability in a science context (food choices for frogs). Students make conjectures about the results of experiments and test them with simulations. They compute **experimental probabilities** for **simple events** using tally charts and bar graphs. Students use a container (e.g., paper bag) with three small objects (e.g., colored cubes) to sort outcomes from a number of draws from their bag according to some criterion (food choices). Then, they construct a tally chart, graph data in a bar graph, and use the data collected to determine probabilities.

GAISE Components

This investigation follows the four components of statistical problem solving put forth in the *Guidelines for Assessment and Instruction in Statistics Education (GAISE) Report.* The four components are formulate a statistical question that can be answered with data, design and implement a plan to collect appropriate data, analyze the collected data by graphical and numerical methods, and interpret the results of the analysis in the context of the original question. This is a GAISE Level B activity.

Learning Goals

Students will be able to do the following after completing this investigation:

- Make conjectures about probabilities of simple events according to some criterion

- Organize categorical data in a tally chart and graph an empirical distribution using a bar graph

- Display their result as a fraction of some specific outcome to occur and test their conjectures

- Compare fractions by comparing empirical probabilities (expressed as fractions) and associate larger (smaller) fractions with events being more likely (less likely) to occur

- Learn about small frogs' living environment and eating habits (mostly insects, worms, and snails)

Common Core State Standards for Mathematical Practice

1. Make sense of problems and persevere in solving them.
2. Reason abstractly and quantitatively.
3. Construct viable arguments and critique the reasoning of others.
4. Model with mathematics.

Common Core State Standards Grade Level Content

7.SP.5 Understand that the probability of a chance event is a number between 0 and 1 that expresses the likelihood of the event occurring. Larger numbers indicate greater likelihood. A probability near 0 indicates an unlikely event, a probability around ½ indicates an event that is neither unlikely nor likely, and a probability near 1 indicates a likely event.

7.SP.7b Develop a probability model (which may not be uniform) by observing frequencies in data generated from a chance process.

7.SP.8 Find probabilities of compound events using organized lists, tables, tree diagrams, and simulation.

NCTM Principles and Standards for School Mathematics

Data Analysis and Probability

Grades 6–8 All students should formulate questions, design studies, and collect data about a characteristic shared by two populations or different characteristics within one population; use observations about differences between two or more samples to make conjectures about the populations from which the samples were taken; understand and use appropriate terminology to describe complementary and mutually exclusive events; use proportionality and a basic understanding of probability to make and test conjectures about the results of experiments and simulations; compute probabilities for simple compound events using such methods as organized lists, tree diagrams, and area models.

Number and Operations

Grades 6–8 All students should work flexibly with fractions, decimals, and percents to solve problems; understand and use ratios and proportions to represent quantitative relationships; select appropriate methods and tools for computing with fractions and decimals from among mental computation, estimation, calculators or computers, and paper and pencil, depending on the situation, and apply the selected methods.

Materials

- Small blue, green, and yellow cubes
- Small brown paper bags (three for each group of four students)
- ½-inch square graph paper sheet for each student
- Recording form (three for each group) (available on the CD)

Estimated Time

One day

Instructional Plan

✏ Formulate a Statistical/Probabilistic Question

1. Discuss with your students the different natural habitats of frogs and their favorite food choices.

2. Explain that, in some habitats, there are more worms than insects or more spiders than snails. So the frogs' diets will depend on what is easily available. Form groups of students, four to a group. Tell them that each group will be getting three bags representing three types of habitat: bag 1, marsh; bag 2, stream; bag 3, tropical garden. In each bag, there are colored cubes representing type of food available in that habitat: blue, flies; green, worms; yellow, snails. The proportions of types of food may be different, appropriately determined by the habitat.

3. Ask your students to formulate an appropriate statistical/probabilistic question based on the background you have given them so far. Lead them to the question, "Is the probability of choosing blue, green, yellow cubes different from bag to bag?" Or, in terms of the frog scenario, "Does habitat have any influence on a frog's food choice?"

✏ Collect Appropriate Data

1. Place your students into groups of four. Give each group three bags labeled 1, 2, and 3. Do NOT show them the contents of the bags, although you should write on the board that blue cubes represent flies, green cubes

represent worms, and yellow cubes represent snails. Students are NOT to look inside the bags. **Note:** For YOUR eyes only, the composition of the bags are:

- Bag 1 (marsh): 2 blue, 1 green, and 1 yellow

- Bag 2 (stream): 1 blue, 1 green, and 1 yellow

- Bag 3 (tropical garden): 1 blue, 2 green, and 1 yellow

2. Explain to your students that they will be choosing cubes from the bags in order to determine the proportion of flies, worms, and snails each habitat has. Tell them they must choose their cubes randomly. Remind them that **randomly selected** means each cube in the bag has the same chance of being chosen. Demonstrate for them that to guarantee randomness, the bag needs to be shaken well and that the cubes need to be exactly the same size and shape.

3. Starting with Bag 1 (marsh), your students should randomly draw a cube from the bag and record the result on the recording form. **Note:** Each group should have a recording form for each bag. Have the students replace the cube, shake the bag well, and repeat for a total of 20 draws from the bag. Such choices in statistics are called <u>trials</u>. The students should repeat this procedure for Bags 2 (stream) and 3 (tropical garden), remembering to record their trial results on the other recording forms as shown in Table 6.3.1. (The complete recording form is available on the CD.)

Table 6.3.1 Example of a Recording Form (Partial)

Bag Number _____	
Trial Number	**Results**
1	
2	
3	
4	
...	
20	

✏ Analyze the Data

1. Ask your students to tally their trial results on the recording sheet as shown in Table 6.3.2.

Table 6.3.2 Example of a Frequency Table of Experimental 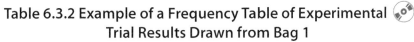 Trial Results Drawn from Bag 1

Bag Number 1		
Color	Frequency	Relative Frequency
Blue	8	
Green	5	
Yellow	7	
TOTAL	20	

2. Ask your students to complete the relative frequency column in each table by dividing the color count by 20. For example, the relative frequency of blue is 8/20.

3. Have your students create three bar graphs showing their trial results separately for each of the three bags. Have your students use graph paper to construct the bar graphs. Note: Make sure your students use the correct procedure to construct a bar graph (i.e., an equal amount of space separating the colors (categories) on the horizontal axis; the vertical scale marked 0 to 1 for relative frequency). An example of a bar graph for the experimental results from Bag 1 is shown in Figure 6.3.1.

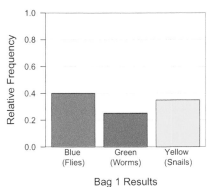

Figure 6.3.1 Bar graph of example experimental results drawn from Bag 1 (Marsh)

4. Explain to your students that each fraction is the **experimental probability** of selecting a specific color (food type) at random from a specific bag (habitat).

5. Ask your students the following questions using their bar graphs and results tables.

   • What is the most likely food choice from each habitat?

235

- What is the experimental probability of selecting the most likely food choice from each habitat?

- What is the experimental probability of selecting a fly from each habitat?

- What is the experimental probability of selecting a worm from each habitat?

- What is the experimental probability of selecting a snail from each habitat?

6. Explain to your students that having more data than what 20 trials yields gives better estimates of the experimental probabilities of the food types per habitat. So, combine the class data for each bag on the board in a tally chart and then in a bar graph for each bag. Figure 6.3.2 shows a sample of class data for Bag 1.

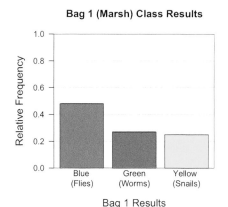

Figure 6.3.2 Bar graph of sample class data for Bag 1 (Marsh)

7. Using the bar graphs, ask your students what they think the distribution of food types in each of the habitats should be. Based on the experimental results, what are estimates of the population proportions of flies, worms, and snails in each of the marsh, stream, and tropical garden habitats?

✎ Interpret the Results in the Context of the Original Question

Have your students write a report that provides an answer to the original question, "Is the probability of choosing blue, green, yellow cubes different from bag to bag?" Or, in terms of the frog scenario, "Does habitat have any influence on a frog's food choice?" Their answer needs to be supported by experimental evidence including trial data and graphs.

Example of 'Interpret the Results'

Note: The following is not an example of actual student work, but an example of all the parts that should be included in student work.

Our biology and mathematics teachers must have gotten together and decided to give us a statistical problem involving trying to determine the distribution of food types for different habitats in which frogs live. The food types that frogs eat are flies, worms, and snails and the frog habitats we used were marshes, streams, and tropical gardens.

To collect data, flies were represented by blue cubes, worms by green ones, and snails by yellow. The habitats were paper bags labeled 1, 2, and 3. The question we investigated was, "Is the probability of choosing blue, green, yellow cubes different from bag to bag?" Or, in terms of the frog scenario, "Does habitat have any influence on a frog's food choice?"

We worked in groups of four and each group was given three bags. The bags had different proportions of colored cubes in them. We were not allowed to look inside the bags. To determine experimental probabilities for the food types per bag, each of our groups randomly selected a food type from a bag, wrote it down, replaced the cube, and did it 19 more times. Each time was called a trial. We shook the bag a lot each time so we didn't bias the choices. To get a better idea of what each bag (habitat population) had in it, we put all of our group results together and drew these bar graphs, one for each habitat.

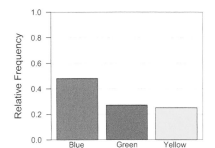

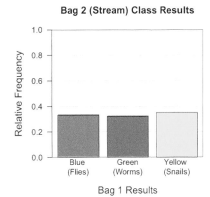

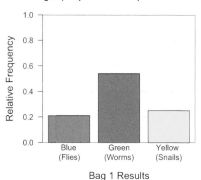

Bag 3 (Tropical Garden) Class Results

Bag 1 Results

We decided that Blue (flies) was the most likely pick from Bag 1 (marsh habitat) and that the other two foods, worms and snails, were about the same. So we thought the distribution in marshes would be 45% flies, 27.5% worms, and 27.5% snails.

It turned out that Bag 1 contained 2 blue, 1, green, and 1 yellow, so the population proportions were actually 50%, 25%, 25%. Our experimental results were pretty close.

In the stream habitat, our experimental results indicated that all three food types were equal. We were right because Bag 2, the stream habitat, contained one of each of the colors, so the distribution of food types is 33 1/3% each.

For Bag 3, the tropical garden habitat, our bar graph of experimental results looked like it would have been determined from a 1-2-1 distribution (i.e., 25% flies, 50% worms, and 25% snails). We were right on that one, too. By the way, our individual group results were not really close to the actual bag proportions, but we learned that getting a larger data collection by putting all our group results together brought us much closer to the right answers. It was neat to see that biology and statistics go together.

Assessment with Answers

One group of students drew a cube from each of three bags that were labeled Bag 1 Marsh, Bag 2 Stream, Bag 3 Tropical Garden. They repeated the drawing 20 times for each bag. They got the results shown in Table 6.3.3.

Table 6.3.3 Results of 20 Draws from 3 Bags

Color	Count for Bag 1 (Marsh)	Color	Count for Bag 2 (Stream)	Color	Count for Bag 3 (Tropical Garden)
Blue	9	Blue	5	Blue	5
Green	5	Green	7	Green	9
Yellow	6	Yellow	8	Yellow	6
TOTAL	20	TOTAL	20	TOTAL	20

1. Complete the following table by converting each color count into relative frequency.

Color	Count for Bag 1	Rel. Freq.	Color	Count for Bag 2	Rel. Freq.	Color	Count for Bag 3	Rel. Freq.
Blue	9	.45	Blue	5	.25	Blue	5	.25
Green	5	.25	Green	7	.35	Green	9	.45
Yellow	6	.30	Yellow	8	.40	Yellow	6	.30
TOTAL	20		TOTAL	20		TOTAL	20	

2. Draw a bar graph of the results for each of the three bags. Be sure to include a title for the table and label the axes.

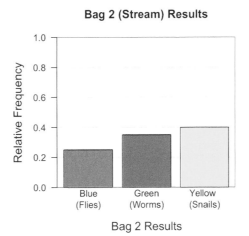

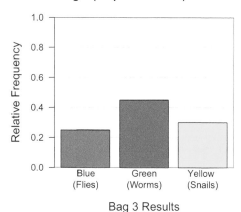

Bag 3 (Tropical Garden) Results

Relative Frequency

Bag 3 Results

Blue (Flies) — Green (Worms) — Yellow (Snails)

3. If you reach into the student's first bag and randomly choose a single cube, which color would you most likely choose? Explain your answer.
Blue. Blue has the highest relative frequency. It is the mode color.

4. If you reach into the student's second bag and randomly choose a single cube, which color would you most likely choose? Explain your answer.
Yellow (.4), but it might be green (.35).

5. If you reach into the student's third bag and randomly choose a single cube, which color would you most likely choose? Explain your answer.
Green. Green has the highest relative frequency. It is the mode color.

6. Based on these sample results, what do you think the proportion of blue, green, and yellow cubes in each of the three bags is? Explain your answer.
It looks like the first bag might be 50-25-25%; the second bag might be uniform (evenly distributed); and the third bag might be 25-50-25%, but I would like to have more data to be sure.

Extension

Note: These questions refer to the data in the assessment.

1. If you reach into the student's second bag and randomly choose a single ball, what are the chances of getting a blue or green ball? Explain your answer. 12/20. Add the number of blue and number of green and divide by total number, 20.

2. If you reach into the student's third bag and randomly choose a single ball, what are the chances you do not get a blue ball? Explain your answer.
15/20. Add the number for the other two colors and divide by 20.

3. Which bag would you choose to draw one cube from to give you the best chance of drawing a green cube? Explain your answer. Bag 3. The number of green is higher than the other two colors.

Additional Extensions

1. Have each group of students construct their own "habitats" (bags with small cubes). Each group should then write probability questions based on their habitats. Allow groups to change the type of animal(s) eating and being eaten. The groups can then exchange their bags and questions.

2. Play the Leap Frog Game at *www.beaconlearningcenter.com/WebLessons/ LeapFrog/default.htm*. The object of the game is to "leap" the frogs from one side of the pond to the other. The color of frog resulting from a spin of a spinner gets to "leap" another step across the pond. The first frog to get to the other side wins the game. Which spinner should be chosen to win the game?

3. Give students a "secret" habitat whose contents are not revealed. Students are to repeat the experiment, collect data, and then make a prediction about the number of snails, worms, and flies, knowing only the total number of cubes in the bag. Students should justify their decisions with numbers and sentences.

References

Franklin, C., G. Kader, D. Mewborn, J. Moreno, R. Peck, M. Perry, and R. Scheaffer. 2007. *Guidelines for assessment and instruction in statistics education (GAISE) report: A pre-k–12 curriculum framework*. Alexandria, VA: American Statistical Association. *www.amstat.org/education/gaise*.

National Council of Teachers of Mathematics. 2000. *Principles and standards for school mathematics*. Reston, VA: National Council of Teachers of Mathematics.

Common Core State Standards for Mathematics. www.corestandards.org.

Leap Frog Game. *www.beaconlearningcenter.com/WebLessons/LeapFrog/default. htm*.

USGS Frog Quizzes. *www.pwrc.usgs.gov/frogquiz*.

USGS Patuxent Wildlife Research Center. *www.pwrc.usgs.gov*.

INVESTIGATION 6.4
HOW MANY SPINS TO WIN THE PRIZE?

Overview

This investigation focuses on determining, by **experimentation**, the number of spins necessary in a spinner experiment to observe a "success." Students will conduct an experiment and combine class data into tables and graphs, draw conclusions, and make predictions based on the class data collected.

GAISE Components

This investigation follows the four components of statistical problem solving put forth in the *Guidelines for Assessment and Instruction in Statistics Education (GAISE) Report.* The four components are formulate a statistical question that can be answered with data, design and implement a plan to collect appropriate data, analyze the collected data by graphical and numerical methods, and interpret the results of the analysis in the context of the original question. This is a GAISE Level B activity.

Learning Goals

Students will be able to do the following after completing this investigation:

- Organize the results of a probability experiment in a frequency table

- Summarize the results of a probability experiment

- Make predictions based on the results of a probability experiment

- Be aware that the more they repeat an experiment, the more reliable their results will be

Common Core State Standards for Mathematical Practice

1. Make sense of problems and persevere in solving them.
2. Reason abstractly and quantitatively.
3. Construct viable arguments and critique the reasoning of others.
4. Model with mathematics.

Common Core State Standards Grade Level Content

7.SP.6 Approximate the probability of a chance event by collecting data on the chance process that produces it and observing its long-run relative frequency, and predict the approximate relative frequency given the probability. For example, when rolling a number cube 600 times, predict that a 3 or 6 would be rolled roughly 200 times, but probably not exactly 200 times.

NCTM Principles and Standards for School Mathematics

Data Analysis and Probability

Grades 6–8 Use proportionality and a basic understanding of probability to make and test conjectures about the results of experiments and simulations

Materials

- Spinner with four equal sections

- Large paper clip

- Recording sheet (five for each group of two students) (available on the CD)

- Grid paper

Estimated Time

1–2 days

Instructional Plan

✏ Formulate a Statistical/Probabilistic Question

1. Begin this investigation by handing out or displaying the "Winning a Silver Car" scenario (available on the CD). Introduce the "Winning a Silver Car" scenario by asking your students if they have ever played a game at a carnival in which they had to spin a spinner to win a prize.

   Winning a Silver Car
   At the school carnival, there is a game in which students spin a large spinner. The spinner has four equal sections: silver, green, blue, and red. Each section represents the color of a toy car that can be won. To play the game, Sarah has to buy some tickets at the ticket booth. She needs one ticket each time she spins the spinner. She also wants to win a silver toy car. If the spinner stops on silver on her first spin, Sarah wins. If not, she has to spin the spinner until it stops on silver. So, she needs to decide how many tickets she should buy to play this game to win a silver toy car.

2. Display the spinner with four equal sections labeled green, silver, blue, and red as shown in Figure 6.4.1. Ask your students to list all the possible

outcomes for each spin and then ask what the chances are of landing on silver with each spin of the spinner.

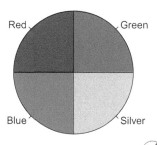

Figure 6.4.1 Spinner

3. Ask your students to formulate a statistical or probabilistic question that will help Sarah. Note that they should formulate the question "How many tickets are needed for Sarah to buy in order for her to win her favorite prize of the silver toy car in playing Winning a Silver Car?"

✏️ Collect Appropriate Data

1. Place your students in groups of two. Give each group a copy of the spinner, a paper clip, and a recording sheet (available on the CD). Model one trial for your students. Use a large paper clip as your spinner, spin the spinner until you get silver, and be sure to record the color of each spin on a recording sheet similar to Table 6.4.1. Finally, record the total number of spins needed to get silver.

Table 6.4.1 Recording Sheet

Spin Number	Color
1	
2	
3	
4	
5	
…	

2. Have each group spin their spinner until a silver outcome occurs. One student in the group should do the spinning while the other records the color result of each spin. Remind your students that their spinner should be on a flat surface. Be sure that they record the color outcome of each spin on their recording sheet. Even though the outcome of each spin is being recorded, it is the total number of spins needed to get silver that will be collected from each group. **Note:** Be sure the students are spinning their paper clips correctly. The clip should rotate several times before coming to rest. This may take some practice to avoid biasing the results.

3. Create a number line that begins at 1 and ends at the most number of spins. To determine the most number, ask your students if any group required more than 20 spins, 15, 14, 13, … Then, draw a number line on the board. Ask each group for their number of spins. Represent each group's number of spins with an X above the number of spins to create a dotplot. Figure 6.4.2 is an example of a class dotplot after each group completed the simulation once.

Number of Spins to Stop on Silver

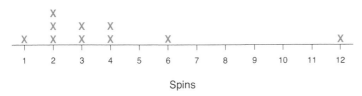

Figure 6.4.2 Dotplot of an example of class data

4. Explain to your students that the more data they have, the better their estimate for Sarah will be. Direct the groups to repeat the simulation again. Have the students reverse who spins and who records. Be sure the new students practice their spinning. As the groups complete the simulation, add their results to the class dotplot. Have students repeat the simulation at least four more times, each time adding the students' results to the class dotplot. An example of a class dotplot based on 100 simulations is shown in Figure 6.4.3.

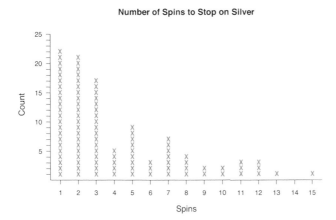

Figure 6.4.3 Dotplot of class data number of spins

🖎 Analyze the Data

1. Ask your students to describe the class dotplot. Be sure they understand what the horizontal and vertical axes are measuring. **Note:** The distribution is skewed to the right.

2. Have your students answer the following questions by using the dotplot:

   a. What was the least number of spins to win the silver toy car?

   b. What was the largest number of spins needed to win the silver toy car?

   c. What number of spins happened most often (the mode)?

   d. What is the median number of spins to win the silver toy car?

   e. Estimate the average number of spins needed to win the silver toy car. Explain how you made your estimate. Note that the "fair share" approach to the mean was described in Section 3.3 and the "balance of deviations" development of the mean was discussed in Section 3.4.

3. Ask your students whether they think Sarah having to play the game eight (or a value in the "middle" of the number of spins) times before she won the silver car is a lot of spins. Have them explain their answer.

4. Discuss with your students what their recommendation would be to Sarah for the number of tickets she should buy. For example, based on their simulated distribution (dotplot) what is the probability that Sarah will need 20 (or some value beyond the simulated results) or more tickets? **Note:** This can be written P(20). Since the highest number of tickets simulated was 15 in our class example, the likelihood that she needs 20 tickets is basically zero, or P(20) = 0.

5. What about 15 (or your highest value obtained) or more tickets? The probability that she will need 15 or more tickets, written P(15 or more), is small since that only occurred one time in 100 trials. In other words, if she were to play the game 100 times, she would need 15 or more tickets only once.

6. Discuss with your students how to determine the probability of needing to buy 12 or more tickets, written P(12 or more). Emphasize that 12 or more means the P(12) + P(13) + P(14) + P(15) or P(x ≥ 12) = 3/100 + 1/100 + 0/100 + 1/100 = 5/100 = .05. In other words, if Sarah were to play the game 100 times, she will probably need at least 12 tickets on five of those times.

7. Ask your students to create a table of probabilities based on their simulated results (available on the CD). The table should have three columns: Number of Spins Needed to Win (n), P(n), and P(n or more). See Table 6.4.2 for the sample class simulations.

Table 6.4.2 Probabilities Based on the 100 Simulations

Number of Spins Needed to Win (n)	P(n)	P(n or more)
15	.01	.01
14	.00	.01
13	.01	.02
12	.03	.05
11	.03	.08
10	.02	.10
9	.02	.12
8	.04	.16
7	.07	.23
6	.03	.26
5	.09	.35
4	.05	.40
3	.17	.57
2	.21	.78
1	.22	1.00

8. After your students have completed the table, display the results on the board. Point to different values under the P(n) column and ask them to explain how they found their answer. For example, in Table 6.4.2, the value .09 in the row for five spins to win was found by taking the number of times a simulation resulted in needing five spins and dividing by 100.

9. Point to different values under the P(n or more) column and ask your students to explain how they determined their answer. For example, in Table 6.4.2, the value .12 in the row for nine spins needed to win was found by adding P(15) + P(14) + P(13) + P(12) + P(11) + P(10) + P(9) = .01 + .00 + .01 + .03 + .03 + .02 + .02 = .12.

10. Ask students to explain why the P(1 or more) = 1?

11. Ask your students to make a recommendation to Sarah as to the number of tickets she should buy. Note that their answers will vary. A possible answer is that she should buy seven tickets because she would need more tickets only about 25% of the time (i.e., she should be safe 75% of the time).

✏ Interpret the Results in the Context of the Original Question

1. Have your students recall the original statistical question, "How many tickets are needed for a player to win his/her favorite prize in playing

Winning a Silver Car?" Have your students write an answer to the question and justify it using the graphs, the calculations, and their analysis.

2. Ask your students if another class's results would be similar if they spun the spinner a large number of times.

Example of 'Interpret the Results' 💿

Note: The following is not an example of actual student work, but an example of all the parts that should be included in student work.

We were given the Winning a Silver Car scenario, in which a girl named Sarah wanted to win a silver car by spinning a spinner that had four equal sections. One section was silver, and she had to use a ticket for each spin. We wanted to find out how many spins it would take for Sarah to win a silver car. To help answer this question, we played the game by spinning the spinner and recording how many spins it took before the spinner stopped on silver. As we played the game, we recorded on a dotplot how many spins it took to stop on silver. We played the game 100 times, and the results are shown in the following dotplot.

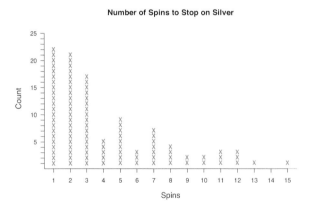

We used our class data and found that the median of our number of spins needed to win was three. We also estimated the mean to be about four. We next calculated the probability of winning for each number of spins and the probabilities for each number of spins or more. Based on the table of probabilities, we thought Sarah would need to buy about seven tickets to win a silver car. About 75% of the time, our dotplot showed Sarah would win if she bought seven or fewer tickets.

Assessment with Answers 💿

A carnival game used a spinner with five equal sections (Figure 6.4.4). A person won a prize if the spinner stopped on the yellow section. One hundred students each played the game until they won a prize. This means they each kept spinning the spinner until it stopped on yellow. Figure 6.4.5 is a dotplot of how many spins it took each of the 100 students to win a prize.

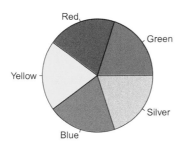

Figure 6.4.4 Spinner

Number of Spins to Stop on Yellow

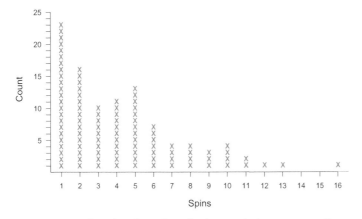

Figure 6.4.5 Dotplot of number of spins needed to stop on yellow

1. Describe the distribution of the number of spins to stop on yellow. The distribution is skewed to the right.

2. Estimate the center of the distribution and explain what this value would represent. The median is four, which is the middle number, and the mean is also approximately four, which is the point at which the distribution would balance. The mode is one, which has the highest number of occurrences.

3. Find the probability of each of the following:

    *   P(exactly 8 spins) = 4/100 = .04

    *   P(exactly 3 spins) = 10/100 = .10

    *   P(11 or more spins) = 5/100 = .05

    *   P(1 or more spins) = 1

4. Andrea, a sixth-grade student, played the game. Use words, numbers, and/or drawings to explain how many times you think it would take Andrea to play the game. I think Andrea will take about six spins before the spinner stops on yellow. The median and mean are both about four, and the dotplot shows the probability of the number of spins needed for the spinner to stop on yellow seven or more times to be 20%. So, 80% of the time, the number of spins before the spinner stopped on yellow is six or fewer.

Extensions

1. Increase the number of equal sections on the spin. For example, create a spinner with six equal sections and ask your students if they think it would take about the same number of spins to get a silver car as on the spinner with four equal sections. Have them spin the new spinner a large number of times, collect class data, and construct a dotplot. Have your students compare this plot with the class dotplot from the four equal section spinner.

2. Using the four equal section spinner, ask your students how many spins they think it will take to get all four colors. Have them conduct a simulation of how many spins until they get all four colors. Collect the data and construct a class dotplot.

3. Have your students go to *www.mathwire.com/data/CerealApplet.html*. This applet allows students to simulate buying cereal boxes that contain one of six possible prizes. Have your students simulate buying cereal boxes until they have received all six prizes. They could collect data from a large number of simulations and use the data to answer the question, "On average, how many boxes of cereal would a person need to buy to receive all six prizes?"

4. Use TinkerPlots or other software to collect a large number of simulations. Have the students compare their class plot to one with thousands of simulations.

References

Franklin, C., G. Kader, D. Mewborn, J. Moreno, R. Peck, M. Perry, and R. Scheaffer. 2007. *Guidelines for assessment and instruction in statistics education (GAISE) report: A pre-k–12 curriculum framework*. Alexandria, VA: American Statistical Association. *www.amstat.org/education/gaise*.

National Council of Teachers of Mathematics. 2000. *Principles and standards for school mathematics*. Reston, VA: National Council of Teachers of Mathematics.

Cereal Applet. *www.mathwire.com/data/CerealApplet.html*.

Common Core State Standards for Mathematics. *www.corestandards.org*.

TEACHER RESOURCES

The National ASA Poster Competition

By Linda Quinn

A statistical poster is a display containing two or more related graphics that summarize a set of data, look at the data from different points of view, and answer specific questions about the data.

John Tukey, in a 1990 *Statistical Science* article said, "Much of what we want to know about the world is naturally expressed as phenomena, as potentially interesting things that can be described in non-numerical words." We collect data to describe and answer questions about phenomena. We present data to communicate our ideas to others. The purpose of a statistical poster, then, is to tell a story visually from the data about some phenomena, revealing the conclusions that can be drawn.

A poster has one major disadvantage, however. Because there is no narrator to tell the story, nor an accompanying report to discuss the data, the poster must be able to stand on its own; it should not have to be explained. For this reason, special care must be taken to present ideas clearly. Not only must viewers understand the individual graphics, but they must also understand the relationships among the graphics and how the graphics address the question(s) being studied.

The American Statistical Association sponsors a competition open to students in four grade categories: K–3, 4–6, 7–9, and 10–12. The first year for competition was 1990. Additionally, a regional structure, similar to science fair judging, was established. This regional structure allows more students to be recognized for their efforts. Each region awards student posters, and then the top posters are advanced to the national competition.

Winning posters, suggestions for improving graphs, and registration information can be found at *www.amstat.org/education/posterprojects*.

Why a Poster?

Statisticians are typically trained to graph data as the first step in a data analysis. Indeed, some would say the second step is to graph it again—in a different way. The National ASA Poster Competition is an expression of this philosophy. Sometimes, it is only in looking at data graphically that observations can be made. Graphs also complement more traditional statistical inference procedures. Posters reflect the **authors' view** of the data. Two posters using the exact same data could look very different.

Planning, Designing, and Constructing a Statistics Poster

The *Guidelines for Assessment and Instruction in Statistics Education (GAISE)* has a framework that can be aligned to the design, construction, and judging of an entry in the National ASA Poster Competition. The GAISE framework components are formulate a statistical question, design and implement a plan to collect data, analyze the data, and interpret the results in the context of the original question.

The first step in planning a statistical poster is emphasized in the first component of the GAISE framework; students should formulate a major question that can be addressed with data. Think of a major question you would like to answer, along with 3–5 sub-questions that will help answer the main question.

Remember that the central idea of the study should be the most prominent feature of the poster. This is almost always the most difficult part of entering the poster competition. So, brainstorm about things that interest your students, things they are learning about, and things they have read or seen. Statistics posters really are an interdisciplinary application. Try to encourage them to ask questions of importance to a wider audience. Avoid questions that are variations of "What's your favorite …?" and "What do you like?" You want your students to generate a question that can be answered with data, and there is variability in the data.

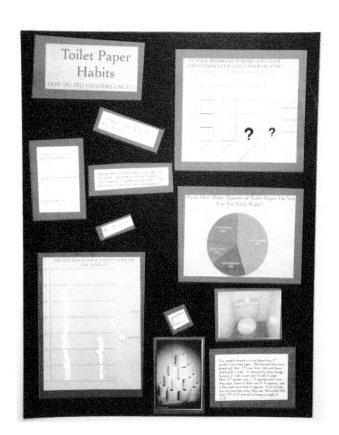

2011 first-place winner for the grades K–3 category

The second step involves the second element of the GAISE framework. Students should decide how to collect, organize, and display relevant data to answer the questions formulated. This really starts by deciding where to get the data. There are several possibilities that would result in a successful poster.

Surveys are a common source. For surveys, topics such as a person's favorite or what a person likes most are not distinguishing. Also, with surveys, students should conduct enough to make reasonable inferences. If you are collecting data from different groups of subjects, use about the same sample size, or report the data using percentages. Secondary data from the Internet or books are also possible to use. Just be careful not to simply reproduce graphs; that would be plagiarism. Students who design and collect data from an experiment are given a slight nod for creativity in data collection.

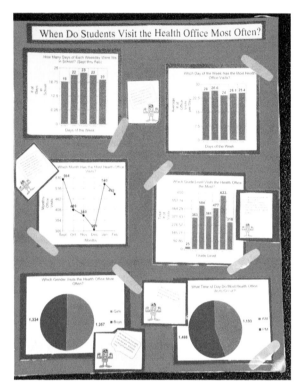

2011 first-place winner for the grades 4–6 category

Maybe just as important as where to get data is to define what type of data to collect and how that would lend itself to graphical presentation. For simplicity, consider a breakdown of either categorical or quantitative data. Is the data categorical, like favorite pizza topping, or quantitative, like how tall someone is? The type of data will dictate the type of graphs that can be constructed during the next step. The former lends itself to bar and pie charts, and the latter lends itself to histograms, dotplots, scatterplots, and boxplots. For categorical variables, try not to have too many or too few categories. Too many categories make for too many slices of a pie chart or too many bars. For quantitative data, make sure to remember the units on all graphs and in all legends.

In the third step—the third component of the GAISE framework—students will select and use appropriate statistical methods to analyze data. The analysis for the competition is mainly graphical. Graphs should be able to be read easily from six feet away and take up at least 75% of the poster space. Create appropriate graphs that show the many dimensions of the data. Usually, 3–5 graphs work best.

Each graph should display a new aspect, not be a different representation of the same data. That is, students should not simply graph the same data using a pie chart, bar chart, and pictogram. A bar chart and pie chart are both appropriate for categorical data. A pie chart is best used when the author wants the reader to compare each category as a portion of the total. A bar chart is best used when the author wants the reader to compare categories against each other. A pictogram is a special form of bar chart.

Finally, the last step—and last component of the GAISE framework—is to evaluate inferences and predictions based on data presented in the poster. Students should place themselves in an observer or reader's place. The graphs should tell the story. Students may want to annotate the poster with some of the conclusions drawn, but the answer to the questions should be clear from the graphs alone. If the judges cannot interpret it, the poster may not have told a clear story. Most of the exemplary entries in the competition pose a research question as the title or the title tells the conclusion of the research.

What Makes a Winning Poster?

Judging the posters is based on the following five criteria:

1. Clarity of message

2. Appropriateness of the graphics

3. Details of the graphs

4. Creativity

5. Overall impact

Following are comments from judges and suggestions for creating a winning poster:

The **clarity of the message** is ensuring that the overall message is clear. One way for students to see opportunities for improvements here is in a peer review. Ask students to constructively critique each other's posters. What do they think the message is, and is that the story the author was trying to tell? Finally, are the conclusions obvious from the graphs, or do you want more information?

> *Dimensionality of the question* – A good poster addresses multiple dimensions of the main title or main title question. While some entries have used multiple graph types (such as bar and pie), this is not sufficient. One improvement would be to graph the overall data and then graph the data broken down by subcategories in other graphs. This is acceptable; however, in the higher grades, the graphs should be based on different questions that are all related to the main topic and not merely a breakdown by categories. This will help the reader understand the multiple facets of the question.

Considerations concerning the **appropriateness of the graphics** are about choosing the appropriate graph and doing it well. Here are some considerations for specific graph types.

A **statistical poster** is a display containing two or more related graphics that summarize a set of data, look at the data from different points of view, and answer specific questions about the data.

255

Pie charts – Be careful using pie charts when the number of categories is large. The pie segments become difficult to distinguish and more difficult to interpret. When possible, consider placing the labels around the pie. It allows the viewer to make conclusions with one less step (going to the legend to figure out what category is represented by which pie segment). This also helps when the colors or patterns are really close and difficult to distinguish on the legend. If you want to make comparisons between several pies, the segments should be ordered in an identical fashion and start at a similar angle. Sometimes, a segment has zero frequency or percentage and does not show up in a pie; this can be an important fact.

Line plots – Line plots, where data points are connected with a line, are usually appropriate when the horizontal axis is ordinal or quantitative, like time. When the horizontal axis has nominal data, consider the impression the graph would have if the categories were re-ordered. The incorrect use of this graph with a categorical axis usually eliminates the poster from award consideration.

Bar charts – While bar charts can be used to show averages, you are really only conveying one number for each group. If the raw data are available, a far richer presentation in the form of boxplots or dotplots should be considered. These types of presentations let the reader see not only a measure of center, but spread and shape as well.

Stacked or cluster bar charts – Stacked or cluster bar charts are used when trying to capture the relationship between two categorical variables. A cluster bar chart is also considered a side-by-side bar chart, and a stacked bar chart would take those side-by-side bars and stack them into one bar with segments (i.e., segmented bar chart). Either graph could work. Try looking at the graph both ways. Pick the way that is clearest in its presentation. Consider the number of categories. Consider if you are using frequency counts or percents (and which kind of percents). If sample sizes are different, this is an important consideration.

Boxplots – Multiple boxplots on the same graph, or with the same scale, can be used to effectively make comparisons between groups based on center, spread, and shape. It should be remembered that a boxplot is a five-number summary and should not be used when the sample sizes are small (a rule of thumb might be fewer than 20). Also, it would be helpful to annotate the sample size on the boxplot graph. Boxplots that are meant to be compared, but are in different graphs, use different axis scales, or are drawn in differing sizes, are difficult to compare.

Scatterplots – Scatterplots do not need to have a best fit line on them, but they could. Scatterplots should be designed so the independent variable is on the horizontal axis. Sometimes, scatterplots are underused in the early grades. If the point of your questions is to show a relationship between two quantitative variables, use a scatterplot. For example, if you wanted to compare the length of your name to the value of your name in Scrabble, a scatterplot is more useful that two dotplots showing each variable individually, because now you can see the association.

Pictograms – A pictogram is a graph used often in the elementary grades. Make sure the graph is aligned to start at the same spot and each symbol is the same size. Consider putting a bar outline over your pictogram; does it make a reasonable bar chart? If not, something needs to be modified. Judges are looking for the connections between the graphs and the **details of the graphs** that enhance understanding.

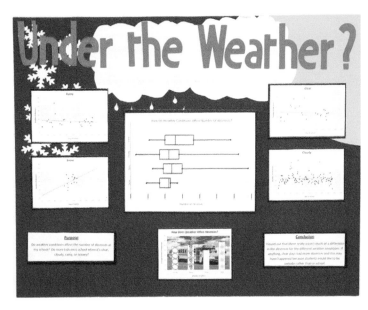

2011 first-place winner for the grades 7–9 category

Frequency versus percentage – When sample sizes are not equal and the author is trying to draw comparisons, it is better to report percentages. Percentages may not be appropriate for some K–3 students; therefore, it is important to try to make the comparison groups as equal in sample size as possible.

Axes and labeling – To ensure accurate interpretation, graphs should be adequately labeled, including labels for all axes. These labels should be spelled correctly and be large enough to read. Most times, it is preferable for quantitative axes to begin at zero. When that cannot be the case because the scale of the data is too prohibitive, there should at least be an axis break symbol used.

Grouped data – On occasion, the totals of subgroups have not made sense when compared to the total group. For example, if there were 30 males and 20 females, shouldn't the total be 50? If the grade 2 level mean is 3.4 and the grade 3 level mean is 3.6, how can the total mean be 3.9? Sometimes, this can be caught by simply proofreading the poster. If there is a reason this occurs and it wouldn't be obvious to the reader, it should be better presented.

Adjusting rates by population – Some data found in other resources or on the web, particularly geographic data, should be adjusted by the population size to make fair comparisons. If the U.S. population is larger than Cuba's, most of the statistics in terms of poverty, deaths, marriages, etc., will be, too.

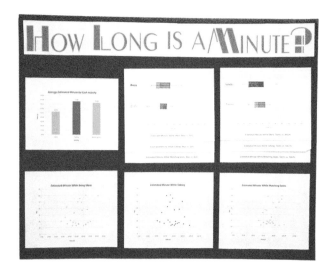

2011 first-place winner for the grades 10–12 category

The use of color – Posters do not have to use color, although color may add to the overall impact. Color is a powerful way to help graphs make conclusions more readily seen. If color is an actual response, use that as the color in the graph. A graph was submitted that described the eye color preferred in a mate by the respondent. The students chose to use the color green to represent blue eyes, yellow for green eyes, and red to represent brown eyes. Imagine the judges' first impression of this data—"Red and yellow eyes!" Using a natural color, say blue for boys and pink for girls, helps the viewer quickly see relationships. Another example for choice of colors might be stop light colors—red for no, yellow for maybe, and green for yes. When possible, identical colors should be used to identify identical categories. Colors can enhance recognition of the conclusions by tying graphs with the same groups together. For example, use blue for boys in all three graphs that are showing boys.

Categorical data – When making use of the same categories across multiple graphs, show the categories in the same order if the reader is supposed to make a comparison between graphs.

Creativity is based on the creativity of the topic, creativity in the data collection, and creativity in the presentation.

Considerations concerning the **overall impact** relate to the entire poster. A winning poster, if viewed as an entire product, is readable from six feet away, is neat, has proper spelling and grammar, and tells a compelling story with four to six graphs (fewer in the K–3 category).

Use of 3-D graphics – 3-D graphics have proliferated with the use of computer-generated graphs and their use in the popular media. However, they can be deceiving to read and interpret. Where does the bar end? Is the pie piece bigger because we are comparing volume? Three dimensions should be used only when the third dimension means something other than aesthetics.

Computer versus hand-drawn – Both types of graphs are acceptable and have won. The tradeoff seems to be readability versus neatness. Computer-generated graphs may be neater and more accurate, but they may use smaller fonts that sacrifice readability. Hand-drawn graphs allow for larger fonts, but may require more time to produce in order to be neat and accurate (straight lines, coloring within bars, circular pie charts). When generating computer graphs, students should take time to make colors and scales consistent between graphs and add to the interpretation. Increase the font size of labels, axes, and titles because posters should be readable from six feet away.

Use of space – The purpose of the competition is to tell a story with graphs. Therefore, the graphs should take up the majority of the poster. Titles can be readable without taking up a third of the poster. Graphs should take up at least 75%.

Chart junk – Edward Tufte used the term "chart junk" in *The Visual Display of Quantitative Information* and defined it as the extra graphics added to a chart or graph that add no value and distract viewers with information that isn't vital to communicate. Chart junk happens when the creativity and aesthetics of the poster become more important than the information the graph is meant to convey. There are annotations to graphs that help readers understand the data better—reference lines, for example. However, pictures used to decorate, glitter that distracts as to whether it is a point or decoration, and pictures in the background of graphs that make the graph harder to read, should all be removed.

Concluding Remarks

Certainly, students can have fun working individually or using teamwork skills. Every poster is unique. There is always an animated discussion among judges since, like works of art, each judge can see different aspects. Rarely are poster winners decided by unanimous vote, but rather by discussion of the good and poor in each presentation. Then, a ranking system is used to determine the winners.

The poster competition is one way to get students actively engaged in collecting data and drawing inferences, both vital steps in critical thinking. The poster competition also integrates many subjects. While mathematics may be the most prominent, the topic can come from any subject. The same principles that guide improved writing—write, revise, and re-write—also apply to good poster products. Artistic skills come into play in knowing the line between good aesthetic layout and overkill with decorations. Overall, many varied skills are required to tell a great story with a poster.

Resources

Bereska, C., L. C. Bolster, C. A. Bolster, and R. Scheaffer. 1998. *Exploring statistics in the elementary grades: Book one, grades k–6*. White Plains, NY: Dale Seymour.

Bereska, C., L. C. Bolster, C. A. Bolster, and R. Scheaffer. 1998. *Exploring statistics in the elementary grades: Book two, grades 4–8*. White Plains, NY: Dale Seymour.

Franklin, C., G. Kader, D. Mewborn, J. Moreno, R. Peck, M. Perry, and R. Scheaffer. 2007. *Guidelines for assessment and instruction in statistics education (GAISE) report: A pre-k–12 curriculum framework*. Alexandria, VA: American Statistical Association. *www.amstat.org/education/gaise*.

National ASA poster and project competitions rules, entry form, and previous winners: *www.amstat.org/education/posterprojects/index.cfm*.

Webinar: Working with K–12 Students to Create a Statistical Poster: *www.amstat.org/education/webinars/index.cfm*.

National Council of Teachers of Mathematics publications: *www.nctm.org*

- *Navigating through Data Analysis and Probability in Pre-K–2*
- *Navigating through Data Analysis and Probability in Grades 3–5*
- *Navigating through Data Analysis Grades 6–8*

Used Numbers series (primarily data analysis): *www.pearsonschool.com/index.cfm*

STEW, Statistics Education Web, ASA peer-reviewed lesson plans: *www.amstat.org/education/stew/index.cfm*.

THE NATIONAL ASA PROJECT COMPETITION

By Linda J. Young and Megan Mocko

In 1987, the ASA/NCTM Joint Committee, through the efforts of member Dwayne Cameron, initiated the National ASA Project Competition. The statistics project is a fun and natural way to meet the educational demands for integrating the curriculum and writing in the content area.

The project competition website, *www.amstat.org/education/posterprojects*, defines a statistics project as "the process of answering a research question using statistical techniques and presenting the work in a written report." There have been three categories: grades 4–6, 7–9, and 10–12. (As of 2012, grades 4–6 is not available.) Single entrants or teams of 2–6 may develop a project. The following six components are emphasized in the judging:

1. Question of interest

2. Research design and data

3. Collection and analysis of data

4. Conclusions

5. Reflection on the process

6. Final presentation

In evaluating the final presentation, the creativity of the project and quality of the written report are considered. Each project is read by at least one teacher and one statistician. The statistical methods become more advanced with each age category, yet, in each case, students selected a question of interest to them, collected data to answer the question, analyzed the data, and answered their question of interest. As of 2012, the ASA/NCTM Joint Committee is no longer offering the project competition for grades 4–6. Following are descriptions of winning projects in each age category, including grades 4–6 as an example of an excellent project.

1995 Winning Project, Grades 4–6

"Do People's Ears Grow Throughout Their Lives?"

This project was motivated by a newspaper article reporting the results of a British study that concluded men's ears do grow throughout life. When the students looked up the published article, they learned that everyone in the

British study was at least 30 years old. Further, men and women had their ears measured, but the report did not consider any effect of gender. Therefore, the students decided to build on this study by measuring the ears of all ages, from very young to very old, and determining whether ear growth was the same for both genders.

The students practiced measuring ears using clear plastic rulers until they consistently got the same measurements to within 1 mm. They prepared data sheets to record the age, gender, and ear measurement for each person. Because the British doctors always measured the left ear, they decided they would only measure the left ear. Then, they began looking for ears!

They measured ears at school and events they attended. One day, when they were out of school, the students set up a booth at a student union of a local university. To get younger children, they enlisted the help of a local day care center. For confidentiality reasons, the day care workers had to make these measurements. The students contacted a nursing home in an effort to measure ears of older adults. This was not permitted because of privacy concerns. Instead, they set up an area in the fellowship hall between services at their church, where they measured ears of all ages, including many older adults. In all, they measured 340 ears (compared to 206 in the British study).

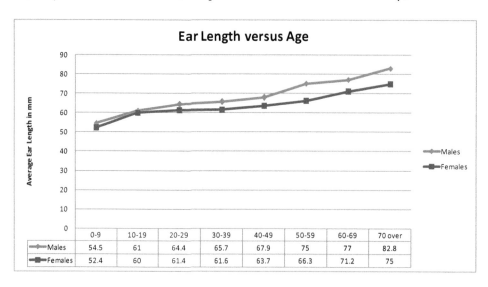

Once they had the ear measurements, they entered the data in a spreadsheet. This is when they began wishing they had not measured quite so many ears. They grouped the data into age categories: 0–9, 10–19, 20–29, 30–39, 40–49, 50–59, 60–69, 70–79, and 80–89. They made a dotplot of the ear measurements, using different colors for each age category. Black dots were placed in the middle of the colored dots to represent males. The students also made a table for male's ears and another for female's ears, giving the average, minimum, and maximum observed ear lengths within each age category. Bar charts helped them consider how many ears they measured within each age and gender category. Finally, they drew a line plot of the average ear length for each age category, putting the female and male lines on the same plot.

Based on the graphs, the students concluded that ears do grow throughout life. Under the age of 20, male and female ears grow about the same. After the age of 20, ears of both females and males continue to grow, but at a slower rate, and male ears appear to grow a little faster than female ears. They discovered that male ears tend to be a little larger than female ears after the age of 20.

In reflecting on the process, the students noted they had enjoyed the project. It allowed them to meet and talk to many people of all ages and sizes. People enjoyed participating in the project, often laughing. Some would come back with a friend who wanted to participate.

At the day care center, the people who measured the youngest children's ears had only measured to the nearest centimeter. The students did not use these data, and it meant they had few children under the age of one in the study. They decided they should have provided more detailed instructions to the day care workers. The students also found they had several new questions, such as Does wearing earrings affect how rapidly a female's ears grow? and Do other parts of the body grow throughout life?

The project's text was slightly more than four pages. The newspaper article and journal article describing the British study were included at the end. All the data sheets were placed in an appendix, as well as a page of the typed data after it was entered on the computer. The four graphs, each on a separate page, were included. Only the minimum and maximum values were used to provide a measure of variation. Since these were fifth-grade students, that was taken as acceptable. For older students, something such as parallel boxplots of each age group would have been expected.

2008 Winning Project, Grades 7–9

"Rip Current Awareness and Knowledge: A Study of What Beachgoers Know About Rip Currents and the Effectiveness of the NOAA, Sea Grant, and LAA Outreach and Education Program"

Knowing that rip tides can be deadly and a major cause of death to beachgoers, students decided to survey beachgoers about their knowledge of rip tides. At the time, NOAA's National Weather Service, the National Sea Grant Program, and the United States Lifesaving Association were conducting an ongoing outreach campaign through signs and brochures to inform the public about the danger of rip tides. So, the students were additionally interested in estimating the effectiveness of this campaign. They wanted to know what proportion of the beachgoers knew each of the basic facts about rip tides and what proportion had seen the signs and brochures generated by the campaign.

An interesting twist to the study was that one beach area, Long Beach Township, did not post the signs or distribute the brochures. They did, however, distribute their own brochure. This is important because Long Beach Township is in the center of the research area (the 18-mile-long barrier island) and, due to the layout of the roads, must be trespassed to get to the outer reaches of the barrier island. The township also accounts for 66% of the 18-mile barrier island that was surveyed.

To determine the effectiveness of the campaign and assess the beach-going public's knowledge of rip tides, the survey was administered to a total of 1,200 people—400 each during June, July, and August. The survey also was given out at all times of the day (morning, afternoon, and evening) and at six beach locations: Barnegat Light, Beach Haven, Harvey Cedars, Long Beach Township, Ship Bottom, and Surf City. The sampling method was not haphazard, but a carefully designed stratified-cluster sampling technique.

The survey was comprised of 20 questions, including demographic questions and questions about rip tides and the campaign. Some of the questions were as follows:

Have you received any rip current materials such as a brochure?

A) No

B) Yes, When I Bought My Badge

C) Yes, from the town municipal office

D) Yes, from a local business establishment

E) Yes, Other:_____

Have you seen any rip current safety signs on Long Beach Island?

A) No

B) Yes, as I entered the Beach

C) Yes on the lifeguard stand

D) Yes, other: _____

Rip currents …

 A) Occur every day on many beaches

 B) Occur only during high tide

 C) Occur only during low tide

 D) Occur only after major storms at sea

What is a sure sign that a rip current is under way?

 A) A line of foam, seaweed, or debris moving steadily seaward

 B) A break in the incoming wave pattern

 C) A channel of churning choppy water

 D) An area having a notable difference in water color

 E) All of the above or none of the above

The researchers used pie charts and tables to summarize their findings about the proportion of people who saw signs or brochures about rip tides.

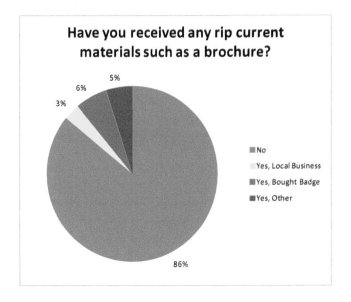

They found that 86% of beachgoers had not received a brochure and 63% had not seen any signs about rip tides. Additionally, more than 57% of those surveyed had not seen a sign or brochure. An interesting addition would have been to assess whether the beachgoers in Long Beach Township were less or more likely to have seen the signs and/or brochures compared to those using other beaches.

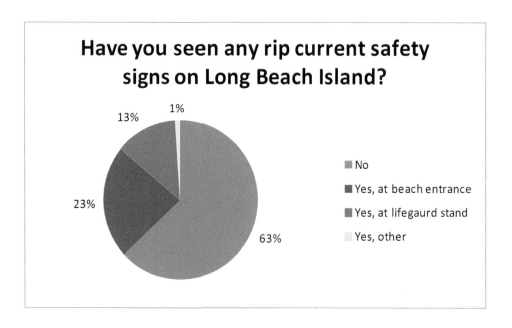

Have you seen any rip current safety signs on Long Beach Island?

1%
13%
23%
63%

- No
- Yes, at beach entrance
- Yes, at lifegaurd stand
- Yes, other

The survey included 10 knowledge questions about rip tides. The percent correct on these knowledge-based questions ranged from 21% to 82%.

The students learned from their experiences during the survey process. For one of the knowledge questions, an answer choice was "none of the above or all of the above." When analyzing the data, they realized that having the two extremes within one answer choice made interpretation challenging.

The students concluded that more outreach was necessary to inform beachgoers of the dangers of rip tides and that many people were not being reached by the current campaign efforts.

The students thanked several professional researchers at NOAA, the University of Delaware, NWS, Coastal Research Center, and NJ Sea Gran and a Long Beach Township rip current advocate for their help during the project. Students are not penalized for asking for professional help on a project, but are asked to address in which way(s) they received help.

The project was 45 pages long, but most of its length was due to a large appendix, large font for the text, and large graphs. The base of the paper was 16 pages long, including a title page, abstract, two-page introduction, 3.5 pages of explanation of the methodology, 6.5 pages of results, and four pages that summarized the results. The remaining 29 pages were in the appendix, which included the survey, summary statistics, and graphs for each question on the survey.

2010 Winning Project, Grades 10–12

"Edifying Experimentation"

Noticing the increasing difficulty of getting into college, four students wanted to know what they could do to help themselves be accepted. Deducing that better studying and memorization skills could increase their chances, they decided to study students' memorization skills and their possible association to grade point average (GPA). The students were interested in determining whether visual or auditory learning memorization techniques worked better and whether there was a linear association between memorization ability and GPA scores.

First, the young researchers asked 34 participating students to memorize two strings of numbers, one for each learning method. For one string of numbers, they were allowed to look at the string, whereas they had to listen to the other string of numbers from a tape recording. The students were asked to flip a coin to determine what learning method they would use first: auditory or visual.

The students were given the number 3741629538 for the visual method and 6409572185 for the auditory method. Both numbers were randomly generated by a calculator. Each time, the students were given 30 seconds to memorize the numbers. They were then immediately asked to recite the number. For each method, the participants were scored based on the number of values correctly identified. For example, if the participant correctly remembered three numbers in the sequence, their score was a "3" for that method.

One of the characteristics that led this project being highly ranked was the careful thought given to the study's design. Flipping the coin to determine the order of treatments, generating random strings of numbers to memorize, and using the video recorder to recite the numbers reflected good attempts to control bias.

Because each participant used the visualization method and auditory method, the students properly conducted a significance test and constructed a confidence interval for a matched pairs design. The careful approach to checking assumptions and clear and precise conclusion statements were also strengths of this project.

Hypothesizing that the visualization method would have a higher population mean number of values remembered than the auditory method, they found there was a statistically significant difference with a p-value equal to 0.0000002. They computed a confidence interval for the population mean difference in numbers remembered between the visualization and auditory learning methods. They found that population mean number of values remembered for the visualization method was between 1.84 and 3.98 more values than with the auditory method, with 95% confidence.

The students also investigated the association between GPA and the memorization ability score. To do this, the memorization score was found by adding the two scores from the visualization and auditory learning methods. The significance test for the null hypothesis that population slope was equal to 0 resulted in a small *p*-value (0.000302), and the students concluded there was evidence of an association between GPA and the memorization score.

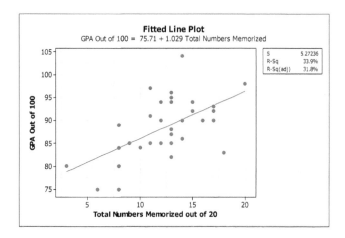

After making these conclusions, the students took some time to reflect on ways to improve the project. They mentioned that self-reported GPAs might be unreliable and, if they did this project again, they would attempt to gain parental permission to verify the GPAs with school records. They also would consider using a different sequence of numbers for the auditory method since some students found the "57" in that sequence easier to memorize than other numbers. Because some sequences are easier to learn than others, the design could have been improved further by generating new random sequences for each student and memorization method. This would allow each method to have an equal chance of getting an easy or a difficult sequence for each student.

The project was 12 pages in total with one title page and three pages of data tables and illustrations. The introduction and project description made up one page. The formal statistical inference techniques used were described and results shown in six pages, and the conclusion was one page.

Final Thoughts

Good projects have some common elements, irrespective of grade level. First, the research question(s) must be clear. Then, data must be collected that can answer the question. As an example, while the research question, "Are boys or girls smarter?" is certainly interesting and clear, students do not have the ability to collect data that can truly answer that question. Also notice that the questions being posed in the studies described above are all fairly simple ones. A simple, well-thought-out study is better than a poorly conducted complex study. As the research questions become more complex, they become increasingly more challenging to answer.

The design of the project's study is important. If humans are involved in the study, the confidentiality of the results must be ensured. If either humans or animals are involved, then care must be taken to ensure none are harmed. Proper replication is important. Careful thought should be given to controlling the extraneous variation that may be present. Reasonable measures should be taken to prevent bias.

Graphs should be used for all studies. Each graph should be appropriate for the data collected. They should be easy to read and effectively labeled. Using graphics such as 3D plots, just because they are fancy, should be avoided. The best graph is the one that helps the reader see how the data answer the question.

For *statistical* projects, care must be taken to provide the best possible analysis of the data. For younger children, finding a measure of central tendency and variation may complement the graphs in answering the question. As students mature, both the graphs and analyses become more involved. Students in grades 10–12 should include some type of formal inference, such as simple linear regression or comparing two independent proportions. As part of that process, they should ensure the following:

a. The null and alternative hypotheses are explained

b. The assumptions are checked

c. Confidence intervals and *p*-values are stated when appropriate

d. Conclusions are stated. An informal, nontechnical conclusion also should be given.

Finally, clear communication throughout the project is critical. The reader should easily be able to understand the research question and why it is important. The manner in which the study was conducted should be clear. The analysis of the data should be carefully displayed, and the results and conclusions should follow from the analysis. Because challenges arise in all studies and investigators learn how to do things better, some time should be spent reflecting on the process, suggesting improvements to the current study and discussing any new questions that might have arisen in the process of answering the present question.

American Statistical Association Online Resources

The American Statistical Association (ASA) is the world's largest community of statisticians. The ASA supports excellence in the development, application, and dissemination of statistical science through meetings, publications, membership services, education, accreditation, and advocacy. Members serve in industry, government, and academia in more than 90 countries, advancing research and promoting sound statistical practice to inform public policy and improve human welfare.

Statistics and probability concepts are included in K–12 curriculum standards, particularly the Common Core State Standards, and on state and national exams. One of the ASA's goals is to improve statistics education at the K–12 grade level and provide support for K–12 classroom teachers. Following are some of the online K–12 educational resources the ASA provides. For more information, visit *www.amstat.org/education*.

STatistics Education Web (STEW)

STatistics Education Web (STEW) is an online bank of peer-reviewed lesson plans for K–12 teachers. Through STEW, the ASA is reaching out to K–12 mathematics and science teachers who teach statistics concepts in their classrooms.

STEW is a searchable database, and its content identifies both the statistical concepts being developed and the age range appropriate for its use. The statistical concepts follow the recommendations of the *Guidelines for Assessment and Instruction in Statistics Education (GAISE) Report: A Pre-K–12 Curriculum Framework*. The website resource is organized around the four elements in the GAISE guidelines: formulate a statistical question, design and implement a plan to collect data, analyze the data by measures and graphs, and interpret the data in the context of the original question. Teachers can navigate the site by grade level and statistical topic. For more information, visit *www.amstat. org/education/stew*.

Statistics Teacher Network

Statistics Teacher Network (*STN*) is a newsletter published three times a year by the American Statistical Association/National Council of Teachers of Mathematics Joint Committee on Curriculum in

Statistics and Probability for Grades K–12. *STN* is a free publication whose purpose is to keep K–12 teachers informed about statistical workshops; programs; and reviews of books, software, and calculators. In addition, articles are included describing statistical activities that have been successful in the classroom. Contributors come from all levels of statistical expertise. For more information, visit *www.amstat.org/education/stn*.

Census at School

U.S. Census at School is an international classroom project that engages students in grades 4–12 in statistical problem solving. Students complete a brief online survey, analyze their class census results, and compare their class data with those of random samples of students in the United States and other countries.

This international program began in the United Kingdom in 2000 to promote statistical literacy in schoolchildren by using their own real data. The program is operative in the UK, New Zealand, Australia, Canada, South Africa, Ireland, Japan, and now the United States. The U.S. component of Census at School is hosted by the American Statistical Association's Education Outreach Program and cosponsored by partner Population Association of America.

Under the direction of their teachers, students in grades 4–12 anonymously complete an online questionnaire, thus submitting the data to a national database. The questions ask about such things as the length of their right foot, height, favorite subject in school, and how long it takes them to get to school. Thirteen questions are common to every country participating in Census at School, but each country adds its own questions specific to the interests of its students. Periodically, the national data from the 13 common questions go to an international database maintained in the UK. For more information, visit *www.amstat.org/censusatschool*.

K–12 Statistics Education
Webinars Meeting Within a Meeting

The ASA offers free recorded web-based seminars on K–12 statistics education topics. This series was developed as part of the follow-up activities for Meeting Within a Meeting (MWM), a statistics workshop for math and science teachers held in conjunction with the Joint Statistical Meetings. For more information about the workshop, visit *www.amstat.org/mwm*.

Some of the webinar topics available include the following:

- A Statistician's Tour of the Common Core

- Exploring Census at School Data with Fathom

- What You Need to Know About the ASA Project Competition

- Math Is Music: Statistics Is Literature

- CSI Stats: Helping Students Become Data Detectives with the GAISE Framework

- Doing Data Analysis in the Middle School with TinkerPlots

- Working with K–12 Students to Create a Statistics Poster

For more information, visit *www.amstat.org/education/webinars*.